A NATIVE BREED

Starting a Lake District hill farm

A NATIVE BREED

Starting a Lake District hill farm

Andrea Meanwell

with photographs by Suzanne McNally

HAYLOFT PUBLISHING LTD.

First published Hayloft Publishing Ltd., 2016
Reprinted 2019

A CIP catalogue record for this book is available from the British Library

ISBN 978-1-910237-24-3

Designed, printed and bound in the EU

Hayloft policy is to use papers that are natural, renewable and recyclable
products and made from wood grown in sustainable forests. The logging
and manufacturing processes are expected to conform to the
environmental regulations of the country of origin.

Hayloft Publishing Ltd,
a company registered in England number 4802586
2 Staveley Mill Yard, Staveley, Kendal, Cumbria, LA8 9LR (registered address)
Hayloft Publishing, L'Ancien Presbytère, 21460 Corsaint, France (editorial)

Email: books@hayloft.eu
Tel: 07971 352473
www.hayloft.eu

For my family
Past, present and future

Contents

Prologue

I recently asked my granddad, in his 90s, what was the happiest time in his life. His answer was 'when your uncle slipped and hurt his back, and I was woken at 2am and told to get up as I was now fully in charge of lambing.'

'Fully in charge of lambing.' That was the high point of his life, a life where he has driven *The Flying Scotsman* from Edinburgh to London each day, and driven royal trains for European royal families, as well as numerous other achievements. This is what it is like to have farming blood in your veins. Even if you are not a farmer, and Grandad wasn't, there is nothing better than being in the lambing shed at 2am.

I was not born into a farming family, but that farming heritage nestled deep within me, until one day I could be 'fully in charge of lambing' myself. This is the story, through the stories of the animals themselves that I have cared for, of how I came to be running a small hill farm in a remote Lakeland valley and the ups and downs of life in the hills.

The Break in the Chain

I cannot tell a lie
There was a break in the chain.
Generations of Westmerian farmers, yes,
But not every generation
Walked amongst the lambs and ewes.

My grandfather, in his nineties,
Lives often in the past
Very vivid to him
Are the memories of 1920s
Westmorland.

Very comforted he is,
In his comfortable armchair,
At the thought of my son and I
Outside in the driving wind,
Hail and snow.

'You are getting the chance I never had'
He reflects
'You are living the life I wanted
But was not allowed.'
And the story is told again

Of the hiring fair
At Kirkby Stephen.
When he left school
He wanted to be a hired hand on a farm,
And offer himself at the hiring fair.

His mother and father
Would not hear of that
And got him instead
A good indoor job
At the grocers shop.

Both parents had been hired themselves,
Had been badly treated,
And had strived to make their own way.
They had their own family, their own house
And their son was not for hire.

'The happiest time of my life'
Reflects Grandad
'Was when your uncle fell in the lambing shed
And at 2am I was called out of bed
And was fully in charge of lambing.'

'Make sure you do what you want to do,
You have got the chance for both of us.'
There has been a break in the chain
But my hands do not know that
As they lift the sheep and feed the lambs.

Generations of experience
Within us all
Instinct and genetically stored experience
Take over and my body works
Without the need for conscious thought.

I am not for hire
I am my own shepherdess
In my own sheep shed.
I will take my chance
And make it work for both of us

Lambsy: Mule tup lamb

Every small child likes a job to do, and aged four on my uncle's farm for the Easter holidays, I was given a sickly tup lamb to look after. Along with the Cairn terrier that I had begged for for my birthday, these two kept me busily occupied all day, which was probably the idea.

Lambsy was the focus of my whole world for those two weeks. On waking I had to wait patiently while my aunt warmed some water in the big kettle on the Rayburn that was the centre of all activity in the farmhouse. The water was then poured into an enamel pail with a carrying handle. A glass bottle containing Lambsy's milk was sat in the water and warmed carefully by the water. As I struggled to get my wellies on, while not smashing the glass bottle, I kept testing the milk until it got to the right temperature, by tipping it on the back of my hand. These were new skills to me, taught by my patient aunt.

I then opened the farmhouse door and shouted 'Lambsy' across the farmyard. From the barn came an urgent bleat in return. The conversation would then be continued as I crossed the yard

'Lambsy'

'Baaaaaaaa'

'Lambsy'

'Baaaaaaaa.'

Inside the barn Lambsy was contained in a small pen made

from four bales of hay. He would be jumping up and down, desperate for his milk. Sitting on the edge of the pen, I would then feed him his milk with the bottle warming both of us.

Inside the barn were also the blue-faced Leicester ewes and lambs. These were not hardy enough to venture outside until they had been inside for about a week after the birth of their lambs, and I rather looked down on these strange looking  cosseted sheep. I didn't know it at the time, but these were an essential part of my uncle's farming system.

His farm was 1,000 feet up in the North Pennines looking out towards Wild Boar Fell, adjacent to the scenic 'Settle to Carlisle' railway line ('Sheep on the line everyone, sheep on the line' was a cry that saw us all stir into action and abandon whatever we were doing to shoo the sheep back down off the embankment).

He was by tradition a breeder of Swaledale sheep, having a pure bred flock of Swaledales. Not only was he a highly respected breeder of these sheep, he was also breeding mules and went on to become a founding member of the North of England Mule Sheep Association when it was founded in 1980-81. This was a group of breeders who had crossed their pure bred Swaledale ewes with a Blue Faced Leicester tup to produce a mule, the ultimate milky mother.

It is often said the Swaledale made the mule and the mule made the Swaledale. This was an innovative way in which breeders of purebred hill sheep could add value to their product by producing mules that could be sold to lowland breeders to cross with a terminal sire, a meat-producing tup such as a Texel, to produce a carcass that butchers would value. This is now known as the three-tier sheep system, and is the foundation of modern sheep production in the UK.

So those Bluefaced Leicester sheep in the barn were actually doing a pretty important job, but I didn't know that at the time. My whole day was spent with Lambsy, he followed me about as if I was his mother. I only had to call and he would come running. What could be more pleasurable as an occupation for a child? At the end of the day I put him back into his pen, and slept very soundly after a day in the fresh air. After two weeks I waved goodbye to

Lambsy, with the promise I would be back in the summer holidays to take care of him again.

On arriving at the farm in the summer holidays I tumbled out of the car, and demanded to see Lambsy at once. I was told that he was in the yard, and raced off to find him. Imagine my surprise when in the yard I found a large rabble of unruly sheep; full-sized sheep with horns, sheep that rushed at me and nearly knocked me over. I shouted for Lambsy but no one answered.

'You'd better say goodbye to him now' said my uncle, pointing to a large unfamiliar looking sheep, 'because he's going now.' Going? Where could he be going?

My uncle explained to me that boy mule lambs are not used for breeding, they are used for meat, and Lambsy would be going to live on another farm where he would be fattened up and sold at market for meat.

Aghast, I stood in the yard and made two silent promises to myself:

- When I had my own flock of sheep I would not be breeding mules, as if even the best boys are not good enough to keep that is something I do not want to be involved in.
- As soon as I was old enough to decide for myself, I would stop eating meat, especially lamb.

This first experience of having a lamb of my own brought me not only tremendous pleasure but also rather a rude awakening into the world of meat production.

Hefted

The ewes settle down for the night
Finding comfort in their bracken bed.
Like hares returning to their forms,
Always sleeping on the same spot.

By day the ewe teaches the lamb
Where to graze and drink, where to rest.
Gently they move across the fell
Taking the same paths each day.

Down from the fell in the in-by land
They turn their faces to the wind,
They long for freedom and their home
And cannot settle off their heft.

Like ewes we are hefted to this fell.
We cannot settle if we leave the land
Our mind wanders to the sheep, the fell, the walls.
We too need to feel the wind on our face.

By day we walk the same routes
Checking the sheep, watching, walking.
Waiting for spring, enduring winter
Feeding the sheep and keeping on.

HEFTED

We teach our children the way to walk,
To feed, observe and care for the sheep.
Feet planted where ancestors trod
As they become hefted to the fell for life.

Hefted, anchored, rooted, tied and bound,
Sheep and shepherdess together,
Generation after generation walk the fell,
We're ring-fenced, hobbled, grounded, home

Hefting and Herdwicks
Eight Herdwick Gimmer Lambs

My family have lived and worked in the hills around the small town of Kirkby Stephen in Westmorland, now in Cumbria, for at least three hundred years. Very few people have ever moved away from the area, or married into the family from elsewhere, so we are pretty much hefted to those hills that are part of the North Pennines, the backbone of England. Hefted is a word that means that something has a sense of belonging to that area and despite the absence of physical boundaries it is unlikely to wander far. Hefting is an important factor for rearing sheep in these North Pennine hills, and in the families who use their skills passed from one generation to the next to care for them.

My grandfather and father are exceptions to the rule, both having wandered off their heft to find work. In order to explain how I came to establish my flock on my heft, several key moments in my childhood are worthy of a mention.

The first moment sees me in York, in school in the 1970s. It's Wednesday afternoon and we are watching television. This is a big event; it's the most exciting thing that happens all week. Wednesday afternoon is our class's allotted time for the television. Every Wednesday we make our way to the television room, and the television itself is wheeled in ceremoniously on a huge trolley, and the blinds are pulled down to exclude the light. We are several minutes early, and we watch a second hand ticking around a clock face on the screen. All fifty of us follow the hand with our fingers, drawing circles in mid air.

The programme we are watching this week is a geography programme showing where other children live around the world. Today it is the turn to show the life of a small boy who lives on a hill farm in the north west of England. The programme starts with the boy coming out of the farm door, and through the farm gate, and walking down the lane with his satchel on his back. The camera pans to show the hills around the farm, with the boy dwarfed in the landscape.

I am left with an overwhelming feeling that that is where I should be, that is what my life should be like. I can't explain this feeling, but it was just an overpowering 'light bulb moment' that I should be living there.

The second time I felt this overwhelming feeling was when I was on holiday in the Lake District. We went on regular walking holidays in the Lake District, and spent alternate days walking and sightseeing. This holiday, in the burning hot summer of 1976, I had been pestering my family to go and visit Beatrix Potter's cottage in Sawrey.

Reluctantly they had agreed, although Dad had refused to pay to look around inside a farmhouse, and had sat outside in the car. Again I had an overpowering feeling that I should be living in a house like this, and told Mum that I was going to live in a house just like this when I was older. I suppose lots of small children experience feelings like this, but I did actually end up living in a very similar farmhouse less than five miles from this spot.

By far the most powerful feeling came when I visited the Rusland Valley for the first time. The Rusland Valley lies between Lake Windermere and Coniston Water, in a little frequented part of the Lake District. As it does not have a lake it is not a magnet for tourists, and the narrow windy lanes through wooded valleys are difficult to navigate without becoming disorientated. The valley is unusual in that it retains much of its ancient woodland, which is coppiced and managed in ways that are beneficial to its wildlife including a herd of native red deer that have lived successfully there without having to be reintroduced since the 1500s. Rewilding is not really on the agenda in Rusland, it's never really been tamed.

My new husband Antony and I, and our friend Brendan, were driving around Rusland in 1993 looking for a fell race. I met Antony at university, and we had moved to Ulverston, a small market town, on the edge of the Lake District. I had a teaching job in Barrow in Furness, and Antony was looking for a job and had taken up fell running. Fell running is a sport where runners compete to be the quickest around a mountainous route, often a quick up and down the fell from a local agricultural show. Shepherds used to race each other at these shows, and indeed they still do, but others have joined the sport now from outside the farming community. The most famous and prestigious races are at Grasmere and Ambleside Sports, where there can be thousands of spectators. Antony was second at Grasmere Sports in the 1990s, a position equalled by my son Oscar exactly twenty years later. A neighbour of ours commented 'All the best people are second at Grasmere you know'. It turned out he had been second at Grasmere sixty years before!

So, we were driving along the valley very slowly looking for the location of the fell race, described as 'Rusland Showfield'. As we drove past the farmhouse that I now know as The Syke, I felt as if the world had turned upon its head. I remember looking at three highland cows eating from a ring feeder, and saying to Antony 'I feel as if I am travelling back in time', it was like a cross between time travel and vertigo.

We ran the fell race. Antony came first and I came last, and the organiser called us 'a pair of bookends' which amused us greatly. Little did we know that twenty years later, Antony would be the secretary of the Rusland Show, with his own mini secretary's marquee, on that very spot where the finish line was.

Following on from the race I had a recurring dream which I called 'The Ickenthwaite Dream'. The dream, which I dreamt every night for twenty years, went like this:

I'm waiting for a steam train to pull up to a platform. I'm on the train and jump down onto the platform. I'm wearing black clogs that are like boots, and knitted socks. I have a long brown woollen skirt and a brown woollen wrap around my shoulders. I have to lift my skirt to jump down safely.

I then begin to run, lifting my skirt, up a track and then over Bethecar Moor. Despite wearing clogs I can run easily and swiftly. I run over the top of Bethecar Moor, and down through the gate next to High Ickenthwite Farm.

I think 'Ickenthwite I'm nearly home, Ickenthwite I'm nearly home' and run down the hill. I get to the bottom of the hill, in the Rusland Valley. I turn left, and run

*thinking I am nearly home. I am desperate to get home.
Then I wake up.*

I dreamt this dream every night, having never been to High
Ickenthwite Farm. I stopped dreaming the dream the day
we moved into the Rusland Valley and I have never
dreamed it again since. I guess because at last I was home.

Since leaving university and buying our first house in
the market town of Ulverston within a month of being offered a teaching job near there (we took a piece of paper
confirming my salary of £12,300, the bank offered us a
mortgage of £36,900, and we set off to view and choose a
house); we had bought and sold seven houses previously,
making money each time. On the very day that one house
exchanged contracts, as if by magic The Syke appeared on
the internet for auction. There it was, just like Beatrix Potter's house, and with two acres of land. We could buy the
house as a cash purchase with the money that we had made
from the other houses, in combination with Brendan, a fell
running friend of ours, who wanted to buy the barn con-
version next door.

We turned up at the house and persuaded the owners not
to go to auction, and within seven days we were the proud
owners of a farmhouse that needed renovating. It took almost a year to renovate the house as the whole interior had
to be removed due to rot, treated, stored and replaced where
possible.

The house is a typical Cumbrian longhouse, you enter
through the 'downhouse' that is now our kitchen, and in the
kitchen there are three partitions where the cows would
have lived. These are now a shower room, larder and

boot/dog room. There is then a parlour that you step up into. The cows would have also provided heat for the house, and dried the hay stored above in the hay barn. I don't think that would be a bad arrangement, one of my favourite places to be in the whole world is in a warm, cosy cow barn in the winter, feeding the cows.

We attempted to move in before the water system, from a private supply, was fully plumbed in. It proved to be impossible, so we had to temporarily vacate to a local hotel while the renovations were completed. This was the beginning of many sagas with the water supply.

When we moved into the house the only animals that I had were four alpacas and two Shetland ponies. I had bought the alpacas as I was attracted by their cute faces, and the fact that I could produce knitwear from their fleeces, as they didn't have to be sold for meat. The ponies had been bought to eat up the grass that the alpacas turned their noses up at.

I now had time and space to think about starting a flock of sheep. We only had two acres of land that came with the house, but I had managed to rent more land locally for the sheep. Not wanting to breed sheep purely for meat, and not wanting to breed mules after my experience with Lambsy, I wanted to establish a pedigree flock for breeding. My son Hector was also keen to build up a flock, and as it would take more than one generation to build up a quality flock his enthusiasm was essential. It is not an exaggeration to say that a quality flock of sheep will typically take three to four generations to produce on a hill farm. Nothing is instant in the world of sheep.

We now had to choose a breed, Herdwicks were the obvious choice. Not only was there the Beatrix Potter connection (she had become the President of the Herdwick Sheep Breeders Association and supported the future of this breed by insisting that her farms which were bought with the proceeds of her books should always have Herdwick sheep), they are also one of the local breeds in Cumbria.

Cumbria has two breeds of native sheep, the Herdwick and Rough Fell, while the Swaledale from North Yorkshire has been bred for many generations so is also considered local. The Herdwick is believed to have been brought to Cumbria by the Vikings, and is found hefted to the central fells of the Lake District. Hefting is a system by which the sheep have learnt over time to stay to a particular area of unenclosed land. Although there are no physical boundaries on the high fells, the sheep stay in their area and do not wander off. They pass on this knowledge to their progeny.

Our house was built around 1565, after families were allowed to settle permanently in the area and build houses following the dissolution of the monasteries. The valley had been settled by Vikings, landing at Greenodd (the Green Place), and Ranulf's tribe had settled in Ranulfsland, now Rusland. You can still see Ranulf's stone near Hulleter Farm, commemorating the tribal leader.

Crucial to the ability to settle was the invention of haymaking. Prior to the knowledge of how to dry grass grown in the summer to use for feed in the winter, farmers had only lived in the valley during the summer months. The valleys were considered inhospitable in the winter. I have a lot of sympathy with this view.

Once the valley was populated permanently a grazing system evolved whereby each farm was allocated grazing rights on common land, and turbary rights to cut peat for domestic heating and cooking. Oatcakes were made on the open fire. Our house had turbary rights on Rusland Moss, and grazing rights on Helvellyn. Helvellyn is nineteen miles away. Farms in the valley bottom with good grass would 'overwinter' young sheep (hoggs) from farms in the central lakes, and in return would be allowed to graze their sheep on the central fells in the summer when their fields at home were 'shut up' (free from animals) to make hay. These were flocks of Herdwick sheep.

One can only imagine the effort involved in walking the flock to Hawkshead one day, then to Grasmere the next, then to West Head Farm. A good friend of ours lives and farms today at West Head Farm. Sadly these grazing rights were lost with the creation of Thirlmere reservoir; the last sheep were walked in the 1890s. This leaves our farm without grazing rights. Those higher up the valley sides, such as Ickenthwaite, have grazing rights on Bethecar Moor. There would be no point in them having the reciprocal arrangement with the farms in the central Lake District, as their land is not good enough to over-winter young sheep in return.

The turbary rights have similarly been lost, as Rusland Moss is now a Site of Special Scientific Interest that is valuable as a source of carbon capture. Instead of a peat fire the house is now heated by an air source heat pump.

Herdwicks have a history that is interwoven with the history of our valley, and I was keen to establish my own flock. I bought eight gimmer lambs from a farmer in Patterdale with an excellent reputation for breeding quality sheep. Throughout their first winter they behaved impeccably, staying on their rented land, eating a little hay and thriving. This winter can certainly be described as 'challenging' for us living at The Syke. The previous owners had assured us that we would hardly ever get snow because we were in the valley bottom, less than 100m above sea level. There was a lot of talk about snow in December, and one farmer had said to me 'if it comes now it will stick for a month'. An idle comment, but one that was prophetic.

We had installed the air source heat pump when we renovated the house; this takes warm air from outside and uses it to heat the house. We were warned that it may not function below -1 degrees, and so had also installed a solid fuel Rayburn. Snow is not bad on its own, but snow and freezing temperatures as low as -18 degrees conspired against us. The snow lay on the roads, on top of sheet ice, for over a month. We quickly had to become experts at not braking whilst driving slowly on windy lanes. The air source heat pump did not come on for about four weeks, so we became totally focused on keeping the Rayburn lit. It was almost a Medieval existence.

The private water supply we had also froze up for over four weeks, meaning that much of the day was spent carrying wood and water. Water for washing had to be carried from the stream at the side of the house and heated up in an enormous stockpot on the top of the Rayburn. I asked for permission at school for three boys to go in non-uniform and they wore all their clothes in turn as it was impossible to wash anything. Even going to the toilet became a chore, as you had to carry a bucket of water into the house before you went to the toilet so that you could flush it.

Listening to BBC Radio Cumbria in the kitchen I heard a lady phoning in complaining that her water had gone off that day and it was impossible to live without water. I phoned in and described our water situation very cheerfully, explaining about heating the water on the wood stove. The radio station then made a 'jingle' out of my voice, it went something like this:

Cumbrian resilience
'Well we've had no water for four weeks now'
Cumbrian people
'Its fine, we just get on and help each other'
Cumbrian determination
'We carry the water in and heat it up on a wood burning stove'
Cumbria at its best. Radio Cumbria.

I was very surprised when I was driving along and the jingle came on one day. I don't mind being 'Cumbria at its best' though.

Throughout all this activity the Herdwicks had behaved themselves impeccably, surviving with ease, as you would expect a Cumbrian hill sheep to do. When spring came, however, it was a different story. This is the time when traditionally the Herdwick hoggs would have returned to the fell to live with their mothers, having overwintered in a valley. These hoggs knew that, don't ask me how, but they did. They got 'spring fever' and would not stay in their field.

Each day we would have to hunt them down, walk them home and fasten them in. During the night you would hear the sound of footsteps going past the open bedroom window, as they attempted to find their way back to their heft in Patterdale. I'm very surprised that Beatrix Potter did not write an animal story about hefted Herdwicks, there is plenty of available material!

We would have to drive in the direction of Patterdale to find them. You could literally set your compass and follow a bearing in order to find them. As an academic exercise in observing the behaviour of hefted sheep it would have been fascinating, but as a would be sheep breeder it was infuriating, especially for my husband who worried about them causing an accident on the roads, and for other farmers whose walls they were destroying.

One day I began my familiar drive towards Patterdale, but the sheep could not be found. Frantic, I drove around all the roads near Hawkshead, and down towards the ferry. Surely they could not have travelled as foot passengers on the car ferry? The Herdwicks were nowhere to be seen. We looked for them for five days, after which I noticed one of my neighbours laughing at me and thought 'he's got my sheep'. My sheep had been impounded for bad behaviour, but at least they were safe.

Coincidentally, on the same day that I found them, I received an email from the breeder asking how I was getting on with them. She offered to buy them back, at 100 pounds each. They had been bought for 80 pounds each. I agreed to meet her at the ferry the following day. My neighbour helped me to load them, but typically one of the Herdwicks was missing from the trailer when we got to the ferry. 640 pounds for eight Herdwicks, sold for 700 pounds for seven Herdwicks , making £60 pounds. Sixty ponds profit, minus the hay they had eaten over the winter, and the rent for the field. It could have been worse. The greatest sadness was that I had to sell them without having the opportunity to breed from them. I was not 'fully in charge of lambing' yet.

It is never going to be an easy task to establish a pedigree flock of hill sheep. Lake District farms are sold with hefted flocks for good reason, because these sheep are not only hefted to that particular piece of land, but also because through a 'survival of the fittest' way of natural selection they are resilient to the diseases and perils that lurk there. They are adapted to the land and the climate. It takes generations to breed a prize-winning flock, but in my mind I was £60 in profit and keen to try another breed of sheep.

Whilst writing this chapter my mind kept returning to that one sheep that was lost when they were sold. My neighbour and I had agreed that he would keep the sheep in return for rounding them up and moving them. I wondered if he ever found her, and thought that the next time I saw him I would ask about her and whether he still had her.

In my little daydream I would buy her back, and she would now be elderly and be able to live here.

Before I even got to see my neighbour, however, I received an email from the secretary of a Welsh sheep breed that I had made a website for. At the end of the email he said, 'it appears that I possibly bought one of your Herdwicks. She's been inside for the last three weeks just to ensure that I know where she is.' He went on to explain how he had bought her from my neighbour at an auction. Small world, and I am very happy to think of her in Snowdonia. It will be a long walk back to Patterdale from there though.

Reserve Champion

Preparation for the shows
Begins at lambing time.
Slowly a show team is assembled
In the mind of the shepherd.
Substitutions made, alterations debated.
From April to August, the team evolves.

By mid-summer
The shepherd is almost
Convinced of his team,
But a broken horn
Chipped tooth, tatty fleece
Can change everything.

Two weeks before the show
Preparations begin in earnest.
White must be white,
Stray hairs plucked,
Black must be black,
Fleeces must be clean.

Two days before the show
The team is brought inside
For final, secret, preparations.
Horns, testicles and teeth.
All must be clean
All must be perfect.

Show day itself
Is all about pride.
The pride you have in your flock,
The pride in your heritage,
And the pride when you
Win a rosette.

Hawkshead Show Reserve Champion,
A large blue rosette
And a bucket full of pride.
I am elated, dizzy with joy,
A proud shepherdess
With a handsome flock and sheepdog.

But Reserve Champion
Is only one step away from Champion.
One step from Beatrix Potter's rose bowl.
I have one step to make to get there,
And already on the way home from the show
I am planning next year's team.

Reserve Champion,
Were there ever two words
To elicit such conflicting emotion?
Something to be celebrated,
But with one eye on the future,
With one eye on the rose bowl.

Showing Shetland Sheep
Fourteen Shetland ewes, one Shetland tup

I knew from attending Ravenstonedale Show with my uncle and family, that a show basically IS the culture of that area, and I was keen to breed sheep that I could show at our local agricultural shows.

Visiting local shows, Shetland sheep had caught my eye. I thought that both my two younger boys and myself would be able to handle and show the sheep as they are small but sturdy, and so we began collecting Shetland sheep.

Shetland sheep are a small, thrifty sheep that originate from the Shetland Isles off the coast of Scotland. Their attraction for me was two fold: one they produce excellent quality wool for craftwork, and two you can have a lot of fun breeding animals with different colours and markings. Each of the colours and markings have their own description in Gaelic, so a brown sheep is called a 'moorit', a badger faced a 'katmoget', etc. The Shetland Sheep Society produces an excellent poster illustrating all the colours and marking combinations.

It is amazing that once you express an interest in a particular breed of sheep, Land Rovers will start arriving at your door with 'top quality pedigree sheep' in their boot for sale. These sheep have usually 'lost' their pedigree papers, and are being shown to you inside a car for good reason – they invariably limp when you put them out into your fields.

After several dubious back-of-a-Land Rover purchases we managed to establish for ourselves a good selection of ewes bought privately and from rare breed sales. We bought a tup of excellent quality from a respected breeder and were waiting in the spring of 2013 for our first batch of Shetland lambs.

Exactly one week before these fantastic ladies were due to start lambing, we had snow like I have never seen before in my life. Snow that blew in drifts of over eight feet deep. We walked the sheep into our small stables through snow that was way above their head height. Thankfully they could all squash into our stable building. We had planned to lamb outside, but there was now no question of that.

Several of our neighbours lost entire flocks of sheep that had sheltered in valleys and had snow drifts blown over them. The snow was so deep that they could literally not get near the sheep, until the snow melted revealing the horror of their dead bodies.

Two of our sheep collapsed on the walk into the stables. We carried these two into the building. They never recovered and died shortly after lambing, but otherwise we escaped disaster. A healthy crop of lambs was born, and were shown at local shows that year. We managed to win several rosettes in the rare breed classes.

Agricultural and horticultural shows have a long tradition and a thriving future in Cumbria. Most valleys have their own shows. Here in Rusland we have a show on the third Saturday in August, where there are classes for horticultural and craft exhibits, and a whole range of sports. There are track races, fell races, wrestling, hound trials, craft competitions for adults and children and a whole range of horticultural competitions.

The show field becomes a mini village of marquees which are put up the week before the show by local residents, then removed and put up at Hawkshead Agricultural

Show which is always the following Tuesday.

Agricultural shows may be 'Shepherds Meets' where the classes are all for sheep and dogs, or 'shows' where there are classes for sheep, cows, ponies, poultry, pigs, etc. Friendships are made and renewed at shows by exhibitors. Prizes are presented, tales are told, a great quantity of beer is drunk, and rosettes for winning animals are taken home with pride.

As a child I won the 'best dog' category at Ravenstonedale Show. So far I have won Reserve Champion sheepdog at Hawkshead Show, I dream that one day I will win the Beatrix Heelis (Potter) rose bowl for the best working dog.

So the Shetland sheep were great for showing, but as time went on it became apparent that the sheep are not really suited to our climate here in the Lake District. It may be that it is too wet here in comparison to their native land, I don't know, but they displayed a remarkable capacity to die unexpectedly.

We became experts at dealing with a variety of sheep illnesses, eventually coming to the conclusion that we would have to look elsewhere for our future proof flock of sheep. The interaction of a native animal with its environment was beginning to fascinate me above all else, and these sheep had not evolved over centuries to suit the Cumbrian climate like the Herdwicks had. On a positive note, we had now bred some prize winning lambs, and sold some privately over the internet. Our skills and confidence were growing, and we were ready to take on a new challenge.

Lambing

It's two weeks into lambing
And time for the 2am feed.
I lie awake watching the clock tick over
Having perfected the art
Of waking and sleeping on demand.
Two o'clock, roll out of bed.

Overalls on over pajamas,
Downstairs to slide the kettle
Across the hob in the dark.
Milk is mixed slowly and carefully
Carried round to the barn
Inside my coat like a hot water bottle.

The lambs jump up, shake and cry,
Pushing and jostling for their teat.
Younger, weaker lambs have to be
Cradled and taught how to suck.
Once I've counted them all
I can relax on a straw bale seat.

A NATIVE BREED

Never rushed, never hurried
Night time feeds have their own pace,
Their own melody, time spins out
Across the centuries and I contemplate
The shepherdess 500 years ago,
In this very barn feeding her lambs.

She had the same skills, the same tools,
The same concerns as me.
Then my mind wanders to cities,
Hospitals, nightclubs, factories,
People up and working in the night
Do they think of me, of shepherds in the hills?

A stranger could walk into these barns
During any April night of the last 500 years
And see a shepherdess feeding a lamb.
Are we out of step, are we lost in time?
It's lambing time, it's lack of sleep
It makes you think and fall through time.

Focus on the basics, on the core
Eat, drink, sleep and fill the stove.
Keep the fire on and the kettle full.
Mix the milk, feed the lambs,
Check the ewes, bring them in to lamb.
New life, old routines, the years roll on.

Rough Fell Sheep

Six Rough Fell gimmer lambs, 24 Rough Fell
shearling ewes, two Rough Fell tup lambs

You might think that after the escaping Herdwicks, and the
dying Shetlands, we would be very happy to stop keeping
sheep. On the contrary, Hector and I were now well and
truly addicted to keeping sheep, showing sheep and breeding a quality flock for the future.

What we were looking for was a sheep with the heritage
of the Herdwick, coupled with the ability to thrive on our
Cumbrian land, along with the interesting markings of the

Shetland. It had to be a sheep that was commercially viable and could build us a future. The commercial aspect became more important as we had recently bought a hay meadow, 25 acres of rough grazing and some fell rights for 60 sheep. This purchase was with Antony's pension fund, so the pressure was on to build up a flock that would interest us and provide us with an income.

The answer, as it so often is, was right under our noses. We wanted a native Cumbrian sheep, a sheep that was beautiful but docile, a sheep that would stay where you put it, looking beautiful, but could survive the harshest winters. The answer was the Rough Fell Sheep.

Rough Fell Sheep are native to the Kendal/Kirkby Stephen/Tebay area of Cumbria. The Romans who spotted them and marvelled at how they lived a 'rough' existence on the Cumbrian fells reputedly called them 'Rough Fell sheep'.

They are one of the largest of the mountain breeds, but are not difficult to handle due to their docility. Our first sheep came from one of the most famous flocks of sheep in the Howgills, the Birkhaw flock. These sheep have remarkably 'clean' faces with clear markings, and the Birkhaw flock has won awards for their fleeces from the Wool Board, being compared against sheep from the whole of the UK, which is remarkable for a mountain breed.

Hector advertised for Rough Fell sheep on Facebook, and we were invited to Birkhaw to view the sheep. We saw the whole sheep rearing operation, the fell sheep, the shearling tups that were currently inside, and the older tups that were in the surrounding fields. We were made so welcome, and Hector as a new breeder of Rough Fell sheep was welcomed into the flock. We went into the farmhouse and enjoyed tea and biscuits looking through the collection of flock books. There have been several generations of Capsticks breeding Rough Fell sheep at Birkhaw, and what the Capsticks don't know about Rough Fell sheep is not worth knowing.

They had selected six gimmer lambs for Hector, and to put with these lambs we bought Middleton Hall Penrith, who Hector also saw advertised on Facebook. Middleton Hall Penrith, or Hagrid as we called him, was famous amongst Rough Fell sheep breeders as he was the most expensive Rough Fell tup ever sold through Kendal auction when he was a shearling at 5,500 pounds.

Word spread of Hagrid's arrival. First of all a neighbour arrived to see him, who informed me that he had a painting of him above his fire in the lounge, a painting he had bought at the auction after the famous sale. The next day I heard the sound of air escaping from the school bus outside, as the driver turned off the engine, and all the children and the bus driver set off to see the famous tup leaving the bus blocking the lane outside the house. It was like having a resident celebrity.

All that the lambs and the tup had to do was survive the winter. As I've said, it is not easy to establish a pedigree flock. Having seen the devastation on my son's face as he came in to report 'another dead lamb' and disappointment as Hagrid also lay down and died like a king on a battlefield, we may have been downhearted. Not downhearted, but realistic. We realised that it was no good importing sheep from several miles away, we must find a breeder close to us and buy their excess sheep, as the sheep would be suited to our conditions.

There are two local breeders of Rough Fells, and excess

breeding sheep are sold at the draft ewe sale at Junction 36 auction mart (the new Kendal auction mart). One of the local breeders had sheep in the catalogue, the other didn't. Assuming we could buy the listed sheep, that would still leave us short. We drove up to the farm of the other breeder, who did not have anything listed for sale. Yes, he said, he was taking some sheep to the sale; he was just late getting his entry in to the auction.

We arranged to meet him up at Lowick Common at his sheep pens. The mist was swirling around the pens, it was very wet, and I don't know who looked more sorry for themselves, the sheep or the humans. If sheep could live on this common, less than three miles form our land, surely they would have a good chance of survival on our land. We agreed to buy his excess sheep, but the issue of the price was trickier. No one wants to sell their sheep too cheaply, and no one wants to pay over the odds. We agreed that I would come back the following week, and pay him the same amount that I paid at Junction 36 for his neighbour's sheep.

Typically, the sheep we wanted were listed last on the day of the sale. Normally I would go and have a sleep in the back of the Defender. Many naps have been had at shows and auctions in the back of my Defender, but I couldn't take a chance on missing these sheep. Many beautiful pens of sheep passed before our eyes quite cheaply, and I had to keep reminding myself 'they will die, they are not local'. One pen of sheep I loved sold for 68 pounds/head, but I had to let them go.

My grandfather had recently died, and my mum had given me some money from his estate to establish my flock. As soon as the sheep I wanted came into the ring someone shouted 'eighty pounds'. At that point I felt as if the floor was about to open up and swallow me. The absolute top amount I could pay per head was 95 pounds, remembering the agreement to pay the same amount for his neighbour's sheep. At this point, it looked as if I might be leaving empty handed.

To the surprise of the auctioneer, the bidding quickly reached 90 pounds, without me getting a bid in. I put up my hand for 92 pounds; this would have to be my one and only bid. Our entire future seemed to rest on whether the other buyer in front of us nodded his head, he did not. '92 pounds sold' said the auctioneer, the hammer went down. I had a flock of sheep, and a very happy neighbour when I texted him the price I was going to pay him as well.

It is traditional in Cumbria to give 'luck money', so once the sheep have been sold the owner will seek you out and give you some of what you paid back 'for luck'. Both the sellers of the sheep I was buying did this, what an honourable tradition this is. You feel as if they are genuinely wishing you well, and of course less likely to complain if anything goes wrong!

The ewes now had to be matched up with a tup at the annual tup sale. Hector decided that he would choose and buy the tups. No local tups were forward, other than those that were related to our sheep, so it really was a gamble choosing a tup that you think will bring out the best in your sheep, fathering excellent lambs and hopefully not dying himself.

A tup sale is a fun day out if you are interested in sheep. First of all the tups are shown in a mini show at the auction, the judging placing them in order of merit, then the tups are sold, after everyone has had a good look at them. We had chance to have a really good look at them, as the tup sale went on for over two hours! By the end of the sale Hector had seen two tups that he wanted to buy.

Both of them were tup lambs, so they would need another 'back up' tup as their fertility had not been proven. The older sheep, older than a shearling that is around eighteen months old, were sold first, then the lambs. Hector had identified one of the first lambs as a suitable 'back up' and bought it for a very reasonable 120 pounds, so now all we had to do was get one of the other tup lambs.

Into the ring came the first tup lamb, placed third in the show, with his proud owner. The auctioneer told us proudly of this lamb's achievements, including a win at the Westmorland County Show. Alarm bells began ringing in my head.

'What's your budget?' I whispered to Hector

'500 pounds' he replied.

The bidding opened, and moved swiftly past our budget, stopping at 1,350 pounds. 'One thousand, three hundred and fifty pounds, are there any more bids?'. The auctioneer looked at the owner, the owner shook her head, and took the tup unsold out of the ring.

Unsold at 1,350 pounds?!! We couldn't believe it. This was a lamb at six months old. I suppose I shouldn't be surprised as my uncle had recently sold a Swaledale tup lamb for £2,100, but as the second tup that we wanted came into the ring we were like rabbits in the headlights waiting for disaster at the side of the ring.

'Lovely tup, nice sort, who'll start me off at 500 pounds?' No response.

'400, surely worth 400?' Everybody refuses to make eye contact with the auctioneer, and my mood lifts from my boots as I realise that this just might be our day.

'100, surely 100. Thank you, I have 100.' That's Hector bidding, and as I look up several people smile at me.

'100, I have the young man's bid at 100.' As he waits for more bids, the seconds seem like hours.

'100, am I selling?' he asks the vendor. The owner will not commit, he is playing for time and hoping for some higher bids. After what seems an eternity he looks up, nods, and the hammer is down.

'100, sold Meanwell.'

We cannot believe it. There is no stopping us as we race down the steps and to the auction office to pay. On the way we meet another breeder who says 'I loved that tup too, but nobody was wanting to bid against Hector.' Sometimes things do work out, and people are happy to help you on your way. A young man building a flock is a precious commodity in Cumbria, and the breeders are wise enough to realise this. We had become part of the Rough Fell community, and hopefully us being part of that community will benefit others over time. I have produced a new website for the Rough Fell Sheep Breeders Association, and Twitter account to try and raise the profile of our native sheep.

Too long have the Herdwick sheep had all the press attention. I love Herdwicks, but it seems to me that the Rough Fell is very underrated at the moment. Its ability to produce strong lambs, with excellent mothering and easy lambing, with a winning combination of docility and hardiness is hard to beat in a lowland or upland location. It is also the most beautiful looking sheep.

Rough Fells are unique in that they are not only very hardy mountain sheep, but they are also happy to live in lowland areas and smallholdings. They have also been used for conservation grazing by Wildlife Trusts.

It had been a bit of a journey to find a suitable flock, but at last we seemed to be on the right track. We were at the beginning of a very long and interesting journey, a journey that will hopefully take several generations to complete.

Andrea's grandad

Winter Feeding

It's the second of Feb
And I am half way through
My winter feeding.
I have used two haylofts full of hay
And there are two remaining
Plus an extra six bales.

An extra six bales,
Such wealth have I.
Basking in my richness of resources
The days lengthen,
And I can look ahead to lambing
With six whole bales in hand.

The last two years
When we were snowbound, icebound,
Stuck fast, held hostage, lost,
We were ten bales behind,
Now we are six bales ahead
Such wealth have we.

A NATIVE BREED

Do not talk to me of
Summer holidays, exams,
Car servicing, haircuts, dentists,
The miscellany of modern life.
This is winter feeding time,
We feed, we eat, we sleep.

Twice a day, measured out
According to the needs of each ewe,
Increasing every week towards
Lambing time by small amounts,
Weather dependant,
Condition scored nutrition

It might look simply like
A shepherdess walking
Slowly with a bucket in hand,
And a bale of hay on her back,
But the task of feeding occupies
My every waking winter moment

The First Year of Rough Fell Sheep Breeding

32 Rough Fell ewes, two Rough Fell tup lambs

The farming year begins for us on 5 November when the tups are 'loosed' amongst the ewes. This means that lambing will hopefully begin on 1st April when we have some grass growing in the fields, all being well. Grass is essential for the ewes to make enough milk to feed their lambs, so we could not lamb any earlier in an upland situation.

It is quite a skill matching a suitable tup to a ewe, so when our tup lambs were 'loosed' we were hoping for the best, and that we had chosen tups that would compliment our ewes. Both tup lambs were loosed together, as neither was proven fertile. Immediately they set to work, in an exhausting fertility ritual of sniffing the air, sniffing ewes, curling their lip to see who was ready to mate, knocking the ewe with their feet and waiting for the ewe to stand and be 'tupped'. Of course the two tups were often in competition with each other, both following the same ewe and head barging each other out of the way. Our favourite tup always won these battles, and left the reserve tup to hunt out any other ewes in season, so far so good.

Although the tups only work for a few weeks of the year (some will be replaced after seventeen days, others left in for 34 days to ensure the ewes have completed two cycles), this work is very exhausting for them, and they need looking after. Both tups were called over to be fed each day, in addition to the hay ration that the ewes were receiving. It is important to watch them carefully and make sure that they are not getting too exhausted or losing weight.

The tups' chests were marked with ruddle, a thick mixture of oil with pigment in. This is stirred with a stick in an old metal bucket to make a sticky mixture, in a practice that has been going on in Lakeland farms in the same way for who knows how many generations. When they mate with a ewe their mark is then left on the ewe's rear end. The colour of the ruddle is changed after seventeen days, the length of the ewe's cycle, and then if they are marked again with a second colour we may have problems with tup fertility. It is common practice to start with a lighter colour, such as yellow or orange, and then progress to a darker colour, such as red or green, so that the marks can be clearly seen.

None of the ewes seemed to have been marked twice,

so thankfully the tup lambs appeared to be fertile. Not wanting to leave anything to chance, we also borrowed a tup from a neighbour once he had finished his work on his farm, to 'follow up' on our ewes, just in case.

The ewes are very easy to look after during this period, as they are very interested in their food. I arrive in the morning to a queue of patient ewes, gazing along the lane looking out for me arriving. They are also easy to catch whilst they are eating to give any required foot care, medication, etc.

The two tup lambs came home to be pampered until they are required again next year, and in January the visiting tup went home. Throughout January, February and March the ewes were checked and fed once a day. After all the tups had left the ewes, any gimmer lambs that had been retained for breeding from the previous year can be re-united with the flock. As this was our first year for breeding Rough Fells we didn't have any of these, but we did have some Shetlands who could re-join their mothers.

As April approached we looked forward to the arrival of our lambs, and during the last week of March we moved them all onto the hay meadow so that it was easy to check on them. The ewes didn't complain, as there was fresh grass in the hay meadow, and they were pretty heavy by this time and happy not to have to wander to find food.

We check the ewes two or three times a day during the lambing period. When a ewe is about to lamb she will take herself off to a quiet corner of the field, by a wall or in some rushes, and make herself a 'nest'.

Lambing often gets off to a disappointing start, as a ewe will often 'abort' her lamb early for no apparent reason. This happened in our first year breeding Rough Fells, with one of our sheep aborting twin gimmer lambs exactly a week early. Disappointing as it was, we were philosophical and still excited about lambing. This ewe will not be used for breeding again. Sometimes hard decisions have to be made to build up a quality flock; both eyes must be firmly fixed on the future of the flock.

Lambing can be rather unpredictable; sometimes four or five ewes will lamb in the space of an hour, and then nothing for a couple of days. When a ewe starts to lamb, usually a bag full of fluids will appear from her rear end, followed by a nose and two feet. A native sheep usually quickly delivers the lamb, the lamb slides out with ease, and the ewe turns around to lick her young. This is a very important time for bonding, and if possible it is best to leave the ewe with her lamb on the very spot that she lambed. It takes up to half a day for a ewe to be able to recognise her lamb, at first by scent, and it is important not to separate them.

During that first half day the ewe will be communicating with her lamb by making nurturing sounds as she cleans her lamb. Most of the sheep lambed independently, and cleaned their lambs and had them up and feeding without any intervention, which is ideal. One ewe was walking around with a lamb half out of her when we arrived to check them. As we didn't know how long she had been like this we caught her and pulled the lamb out. She may not have needed any assistance, but it seemed better to be safe than sorry.

We did intervene at some point during the first day, to ear tag the lambs and record who their mother was in our lambing record book. The lambs were marked with our purple flock mark, and a small red or blue dot on their head to show if they were male or female, which came in useful later when we wanted to catch either one gender or another for some reason (castration etc.). We do this when the lamb is still rather wobbly and not too mobile, as we know that we may not be able to catch them easily once they are swift on their feet.

A couple of ewes did come into the barn at home with their lambs, usually because they were born in extremely bad weather at nightfall, and I didn't want to leave them outside without seeing that their feeding had become established and was sure that the lamb had a full tummy of milk. Before the ewe is entirely sure of which lambs are hers, in those first few hours, it is also easy for a fox to steal one lamb from a ewe that has just had twins. Anecdotally, it seems as if ear tagging them on the day they are born can also discourage foxes who do not like the smell of the plastic tags, although this is hard to prove of course.

We also bought some 'lamb macs', plastic jackets to put on the lambs to see the new borns through the worst of the weather. If the smell of the ear tags puts off foxes, the jackets may do the same.

Lambing progressed, and became a blur of lambs, ear tags, jackets and sprays. Each lamb was carefully recorded, most of the ewes had only one lamb as they were fist time mothers, hopefully more will have twins later in life. There were no ewe deaths, but one or two lamb deaths. One unexplained, possibly drowning as it was found in a puddle of water, and one which I believe was due to the ewe not having enough milk to feed two lambs through three days of very heavy rain.

One tup lamb also died after several months for no apparent reason, which was disappointing, but generally lambing could be seen as a great success.

With our novice eye, we tried to work out which tup lambs we could keep for breeding, and chose two. These two were not castrated, and marked with a blue dot on their bottom so that in future months we could keep an eye on them. The other tup lambs were castrated with a simple rubber band around their testicles and, once the lambs were well and truly established with their feeding, they were moved off the hay meadow.

As time went on we became more anxious about getting all the sheep off the hay meadow, as we wanted the grass to grow. Three sheep had not lambed, so eventually we came to the conclusion that they were not going to lamb, and moved them off the hay meadow as well. These sheep were given a couple of months to see if they would lamb, but no lambs appeared.

The gimmer lambs were injected with lambivac, a tetanus injection that also gives cover against a variety of sheepy diseases, as these will be kept for the future. At the end of the summer we had exactly 100%, that is to say, exactly one lamb per ewe.

As summer progressed, thoughts turned from lambing to hay making and shearing. During the summer months the 32 Rough Fell ewes lived happily with their lambs in 25 acres of 'rough grazing', just the kind of rocky, undulating ground with a variety of flora to eat that native sheep love.

We had ordered a hay barn that came in kit form, and after a protracted planning process had succeeded in getting 'permitted development' permission to put in into our area of rough grazing. The wooden barn arrived, and a neighbour put it up for us. Immediately that the barn was finished, we asked another neighbour to come and help us with shearing. Teamwork is crucial in Lakeland Valleys, and we help each other out when we can. All the sheep were gathered in the new barn, and my neighbour clipped the ewes. One son caught the ewes for him, and another rolled the fleeces and put them into the wool sheet, a large bag provided by the wool board to transport the fleeces to the Cumbrian depot in Carlisle.

It is a good time to have a good look at the sheep. Each ewe was given a full MOT, a foot trim if needed, some wormer and fly treatment and a good 'looking over'. This 'looking over' was a kind of assessment, an assessment to see if the ewe was to be kept for the following year. My neighbour added an impartial eye to this process, while I would happily err on the side of caution he would simply tell me 'Annie that yow's knackered' and move her to one side. That's not to say I wouldn't move her back.

Ewes that were put on one side to be sold included the one that had aborted the twins, one that hadn't lambed ('two teats not four, that'll never lamb' and another older ewe that hadn't lambed 'knackered, get rid of it'). These went to the auction the following day and made an average of £47 each. One young ewe that didn't lamb was considered to be too small to lamb this year, and was given a second chance.

All the Rough Fell gimmer lambs were retained for breeding, so these were now taken off their mothers and put into a separate field to be weaned. Most of them settled well, two did somehow find their way back to their mothers a week later. There were now 22 Rough Fell gimmer lambs to enlarge the flock. I had hoped for a minimum of 20, so that was good.

The two tup lambs retained for possibly breeding from in the future were moved to the tup field, and settled fine. That left eight castrated boy lambs. They went to the auction the following week to be sold as 'store' lambs, lambs for another farmer to grow and fatten for meat before selling. These lambs only made £24 each, which was very disappointing. I asked the men at the auction if I should stay and sell the lambs in person, and they said 'You can cry in the ring at the price you are going to get, or cry down the telephone later', so I know the outlook was not good.

I had hoped that the money I got from the boy lambs would keep the other sheep in food for the winter, but it was now apparent that there was no way that this was going to happen. It could have been worse though, as I could have ended up with only ten gimmer lambs, which would have been even more disappointing.

The ewes now enjoyed a few weeks holiday, relaxing and getting fat ready for tupping time without the responsibility of looking after their lambs. There was just one final piece of sheep work to do before tupping time, the tup inspection.

I had known that the tup inspectors from The Rough Fell Sheep Breeders' Association would arrive at some time during September, but when a letter arrived saying that the inspectors were due the following morning it threw me into a frantic whirl of activity. The two tup lambs we had retained for breeding were assessed with new eyes. My son and I agreed that only one of them was worth putting forward for inspection. The one that had passed our novice observations was brought into the barn and cleaned up. My son left for the week for college, and there was no way that I could move the shearling tup into the barn by myself, so he would have to be observed in the field.

Tups are 'starred' when they are shearlings, and they then get a special ear tag and can be used for breeding by Rough Fell Sheep members and sold at the Rough Fell Sheep tup sale. Tup lambs can also be inspected by the inspectors to see if they have the potential to become breeding tups.

Three inspectors arrived to see the tups. To my delight, the tup lamb was thought to have the potential to be bred from in the future. Cost to inspect the tup lamb, one pound. The shearling also passed with flying colours, cost ten pounds. It was also twenty pounds for me to join the association for the year, and five pounds for Hector.

It had been rather an expensive morning, £36 of our £180 made from our lambs had been spent on society fees, but we were now fully paid up Rough Fell breeders, and our breeding stock had potential, and that was priceless.

Stone Wall

You were created by our forefathers
Clearing the woods to graze their sheep.
You are still standing.
At night when it's windy
I lie awake picturing you falling,
I know there will be work to do.

Your stones have been held
By our family's hands for generations.
Your stones fit into our hands,
We fit you effortlessly back together.
My son, thick ginger hair upright in the wind,
Works quickly and silently to repair you.

A nod says it's done,
And he wanders off to check his sheep.
The valley is a total scrow,
Walls down everywhere in this wind.
But we are still here, stone wall,
We have not lost the plot.

The Second Year of Rough Fell Sheep Breeding

32 Rough Fell ewes, 22 Rough Fell gimmer lambs, one Rough Fell shearling tup and four Rough Fell tup lambs

A chance comment of my neighbour about needing to keep my flock young 'My father had Roughs on that land in the 1970s and he found that he needed to keep them young, the older ones couldn't produce enough milk off that grass'

made me sit down and evaluate my flock. So far things had gone pretty well with the Rough Fell sheep, and I planned to build up to a flock of 60 on the newly bought land, and eventually replace the Shetlands at home with more Rough Fells.

In order to maintain a flock of 60, about fifteen would need to be retained each year if the flock was to remain young. This meant that after building up my numbers I could be selling breeding shearlings within about four years. Exciting times ahead. Nothing happens quickly in the world of sheep breeding.

Another chance comment by a neighbour 'Have you not found that water trough yet?' led to the discovery of a very old trough built out of slate in the field and fed by a spring – very useful. There were also the remains of a small building, which must have looked right out across the panorama of the South Lakeland fells with The Old Man of Coniston on the horizon.

I don't know what this building would have been for, but I like to think of it as a little 'brew cabin' where someone sat and drank their tea while looking after their sheep several hundred years ago. Not much would have changed in the world of sheep breeding since then, and I imagine someone warming milk for lambs or mixing ruddle in exactly the same way as I do in the little building. Thoughts such as these keep me company on cold winter mornings when I am all alone in a vast landscape. I am not really alone, because I have all the shepherds and shepherdesses of the past with me in my imagination, and in the environment that they created for me to work in.

The Lake District is a man made environment, a human

creation. When you consider all the problem solving and sheer hard work that has gone into clearing woodlands, partitioning fields and setting up grazing routines and common land it is a massive human achievement akin to a feat of engineering on a grand scale. It is not a monument to those who created it, but a working environment where those of us left farming the area strive to improve our lot.

The phrase 'to lose the plot' originally meant to leave your family, and go away to pastures new without looking back. I am determined that I shall not 'lose the plot'. I am here ensuring that the plot continues, partly out of respect for the past and partly to build a future for myself and my children, and partly because it just seems like the only thing to do. My husband says that I have 'found my true vocation'; I think I have just found within myself my family history and heritage. For hundreds of years people had a deep connection to the land and keeping animals. Most families only two or three generations ago lived an outdoor life rearing animals. I believe it is probably in us all, if we choose to look for it.

Sometimes deep reserves of perseverance and heritage need to be called upon to get you through the day. Especially when you have a run of bad luck.

A run of bad luck was exactly what I was about to have. If you remember we left the Rough Fell sheep grazing happily at the end of a successful year of breeding. The weather this autumn 2015, was unseasonably warm. In fact, I would go so far as to say it was ridiculously warm for the time of year. You might think that was a cause for celebration, but not when you are breeding sheep with long woolly coats.

Despite the lambs having had a pour on solution to keep

the flies away from them, the land is heavily infested with rushes, an ideal breeding ground for flies, and they soon became infested with maggots. One after another, we would be dealing with a new case of fly strike practically every day. There seemed to be nothing we could do to prevent it spreading.

A long-term solution would be to move the ponies onto this land to eat the rushes, and hence take away some of the flies. While this could be planned for long term it did not help us out in the short term, with our plastic gloves on removing maggots from poor lambs in discomfort. We also needed to have trimmed their tails shorter when they were tiny lambs. Long tails may look attractive, but are not worth the discomfort to the sheep if a fly lays eggs in their tail. Lesson learnt.

It's at times like this when you discover your true mettle. It's very hard to be dealing with a health crisis, and reacting daily to it. You feel as if the situation is out of your control, but you must keep on working for the sake of the sheep.

You may remember the two tup lambs that we bought the previous year, which would now be shearlings in the peak of physical perfection? Imagine my horror when we discovered one evening that both of them had maggots around their horns. A quick dash to the vets after we had removed the maggots with a pour on solution, and both had antibiotics just in case. Both seemed well, although I was worried about them and got up during the night to check on them, walking about wearing a head torch at 2am, and both seemed well.

Imagine my horror when at 6am I found one of them,

not Hector's favourite, dead in the field. It was a very sad end to a terrible week. At least it was not the tup that we had already arranged to sell after tupping time.

We did have some fun buying new tups and replacement ewes. I had the money from the ewes that we had decided not to keep, and managed to get three replacement ewes for nearly the same price. We also bought three tup lambs, thinking we would use one as a back up to our tup and keep the others to grow into shearlings to sell.

As the Easter holidays were early, the tup went in on 1 November. For eight days he pursued the ewes and tupped about seventeen out of the 35. I visited daily to feed him. On the eighth day he was so busy pursuing a ewe that he would not come over to eat, but I didn't think too much about it.

On the 9th November I arrived to find the ewes stood around the dead body of the tup, who looked like he had laid down like a king and died. I managed to stay on my feet, and plan what needed to happen next. It would have been very temping to sink onto the ground next to him and cry like a baby, but you have to find the inner strength to carry on. Quickly I went home and hitched the trailer onto the Land Rover. I wanted to bring two of the tup lambs across, but knew I would never manage the two lambs and the door of the trailer by myself, so had to ask my husband for help. We managed to get the two tups into the trailer, and over the field to meet the ladies. A different colour ruddle was applied to them, so that we could see who had been tupped by which sire.

It took two of us all our strength to pull the body of the tup into the trailer. He looked magnificent even in death, and I consoled myself with the fact that a lot of the best ewes had been tupped within those first few days and we would have some lovely lambs.

Travelling home we met the fallen stockman on a lane. I wound down the window and told him that we had a tup in the back, and he said he would take it there and then. We reversed our vehicles back to back, and put the ramps down. He attached his winch to my tup's horns and pulled him out of my trailer, along the road and up into his vehicle. All of this was performed right in front of our local pub beer garden, where some tourists were sitting enjoying the unseasonably warm weather and having a drink in the sunshine. I glanced over and couldn't resist saying 'country life eh?' as they looked on aghast.

Thankfully the weather now turned a little cooler, and winter-feeding began in earnest. On every day in the winter my routine is the same. I load up the Land Rover with food and hay, and drive around to the different fields feeding animals, catching them to trim feet, replace ear tags, give wormer, etc. Animals are easily caught in the winter, and I keep all the tools of my trade in the back of the vehicle. It had taken me six years to get to the stage where I no longer had to ask a neighbour to borrow various things; it was all neatly stored in the Land Rover and ready for use.

The run of bad luck continued when I came out of the house one morning to find that the Land Rover Defender had been stolen, along with all the tools of my trade... medicines, ear tags, waterproofs, everything that I could possibly need. The knowledge that these things would be of no use whatsoever to whoever had stolen the vehicle did not help, nor did all the well meaning souls who told me that

my Land Rover would be in bits, in a shipping container on the way to Africa within 24 hours of being stolen.

Most of us have things that are comfortable and familiar, and my Land Rover was like that to me. When the tup died, I went outside that evening and sat in the dark in the pouring rain in the Land Rover with a cup of tea. It was almost like a den to a child, it was my special thinking place. It didn't matter if the Defender was old and battered, because every dint had been put in by one of the boys learning to drive, memories which popped back into my head during the working day to make me smile. Now someone had stolen that connection to my children's childhood. We loved our Land Rover, and it was a very sad day when it was stolen.

I now had to rely upon a wheelbarrow while the police hunted for the stolen car. The wheelbarrow got a puncture that did not want to be repaired, the weather took a turn for the worse with hurricane strength winds. Picture me pushing the wheelbarrow around the valley with bales of hay in gale force winds. It was not an easy time. I also noticed as the days went on that the new tup lambs were revisiting ewes who had been tupped by the deceased tup, so it appears he was not well from the start of November.

Sometimes, as I say, you get a run of bad luck. You just have to 'get on with it' and carry on. Keep one eye on spring, and lambing time, and hope for the best.

Fell Pony Herdsman

The octogenarian shepherd
Slowly pulls back the barn doors
To reveal his new all terrain vehicle.
'Like a wild bird in a cage I was
I needed to be on the fell.'

We slowly meander up the fell
To see his lifetime's work.
The herd of fell ponies are waiting
At the fell gate, having heard the sound
Of the new vehicle.

The beauty of these animals,
Or is it the wind, literally takes my breath away.
I am wiping tears from my cheeks
As he explains how they thrive,
Semi wild, in their natural habitat.

What an opportunity it would be
To run a herd like this.
It would be a lifetime's work,
It has been his lifetime's work,
A legacy for future Cumbrians.

A NATIVE BREED

These ponies have been here
For generations alongside the shepherd.
They provided all terrain transport.
Before the advent of the quad bike
Sheep were shepherded by pony.

Still useful as riding ponies
Desirable for the show ring
These herds are kept on the fell
As a living heritage
Reliant on the love of the shepherd.

Driving home I think how ironic it is
That the vehicle which ensures
That the shepherd can tend his herd
Is the very vehicle
Which has made these shepherding ponies a thing
                    of the past

Fell Ponies
Thirteen Registered Fell Ponies

It's a well-known fact that muscles have memory, that's why you don't forget how to ride a bike. Can muscles have memory through generations? That's the only way I can explain how my youngest son can ride an 'unrideable' fell pony without ever having ridden before.

The first time I took my son riding, he picked out a pony in the field and demanded to ride that one. The instructor was hesitant, but he insisted he could do it. On he jumped, and it was almost as if he could communicate intuitively with the pony right from the off. It was one of the most re-markable things I have ever seen in my life.

Later that evening I telephoned my grandad who said 'well of course he can ride, his great-great-grandfather was one of the most famous fell pony hauliers in the North of England. Great streams of ponies he had. He travelled all over the North of England transporting goods for people. It's in his blood. I taught myself how to ride by jumping down on the backs of fell ponies from trees after school. It's a natural thing for a lad in our family to do.'

This was the first I had heard of our family history with fell ponies. As a child I had been very interested in sup-porting charities that helped endangered animals such as elephants, and yet here was a local, endangered animal with a family history that I had entirely overlooked. Not for much longer, Fell ponies would soon become an enduring love, but first we must tell the story of how we ended up at the riding centre that day.

It is the mid-1970s, and my uncle and I are going shop-ping. We're on an old David Brown tractor with a trailer to transport our purchases, and we are driving over Orton Fell as the sun sets. I can still see that sunset now in my mind's eye. Orton Fell is a vast expanse of common land with limestone pavement, a huge open wilderness, there is only moorland, sky, sheep and ponies as far as the eye can see.

I am sitting in the back of the tractor, looking out at the sun going down and the ponies on the horizon. It is a mo-ment in time that will stay with me, and we were going to meet a memorable character.

My uncle and I were travelling to meet a friend of his, Willie Pratt, who had some calves to sell. My uncle wanted to buy a couple and fatten them on. Willie Pratt came blustering and spitting out of his farmhouse as we drove into the yard. Putting on his coat and fastening it with bailer twine, he set off at great speed to one of his barns. It was dimly lit, and filled with jittery calves darting about.

Every time one caught my uncle's eye and pointed it out, Willie would do an enormous loud spit, and say 'That's a good calf, Alan, that's a good calf.' He must have uttered the phrase about 50 times. Eventually we decided on the calves and drove them home in the darkness, and Willie became the stuff of legends. I would imitate him regularly to amuse my family, and I even wrote about him in my 'O' level English exam.

Over thirty years later as I drive over Orton Fell and into the farmyard I am hit with an overwhelming feeling that I have been here before. We have come to look at some Shetland ponies that we have seen on the internet for sale. As the lady opens the farmhouse door I realise where I am

'Did Willie Pratt used to live here?'

'Aye, lass, you've a good memory.'

Remarkable how these coincidences happen. We had decided to get a couple of miniature Shetland ponies to help the alpacas graze the fields. The alpacas loved to eat the same patch of grass over and over, leaving the rest to grow long. The idea was that the ponies could then follow them into a field and eat up the remaining grass.

We chose two ponies, and arranged for them to be delivered, and as a parting comment the seller said to my son, 'You'll enjoy riding her.' Up until that moment the idea of riding ponies had never occurred to us. We decided that we would like to ride and booked ourselves some lessons.

After the conversation with my grandad about the ponies I began to read up about them. I discovered, although I must have always known this, that there are herds of semi-wild fell ponies in the Howgill Fells and on some other Cumbrian fells. Although they have owners, the ponies live an essentially wild existence, being brought in to separate the young colts from their mothers and for occasional visits from the farrier. The rest of the year they live out on the fell, with only a little extra nourishment during very bad weather, usually in the form of hay.

Fell ponies have evolved from an ancient, native breed of pony called the Galloway which was in existence when the Romans invaded Cumbria. Some local people still refer to them as 'Gallowas'. They were admired by the Romans, and by many other people throughout history. The monks of Furness Abbey used them to travel around Cumbria on, and preferred grey ponies.

They became the main mode of transport for the fell farmer. A pony would be one of his most prized possessions, and would be the equivalent of a Land Rover today. The shepherd could check his sheep on his pony, and carry a sickly sheep back home on it. He could strap some bales of hay and take it out to his stock in bad weather. A pony will instinctively find his own way through terrain, he can smell out a boggy area or sense when there is a deep snowdrift. Pony riders need to be easy on the reins, the bond of trust built up between the rider and pony is crucial, and the rider must let the pony find his own way safely.

Ponies were also essential as forms of transport, to get to church on Sunday and to visit relatives. From my house here in Rusland to Colton church, which the inhabitants would have visited every Sunday, is about a 30 minute pony ride away, and you can see where the ponies would have been tied up outside during the service. Ponies were also used for haulage, and there would have been great trains of ponies travelling across England transporting wool and other goods. Inns grew up along the packhorse routes, and spinning galleries were built onto some farmhouses where craft items for sale could be displayed to passers by. Craft items were sometimes traded for luxury items such as spices, which were imported on the west coast of Cumbria and then across land by pony. On the high fells ponies were used to pull sleds laden with hay or stones for walling which ran easier over muddy or snowy land.

My great-great-grandfather ran such a group of ponies from Great Asby in Westmorland, and my grandad can remember the ponies when he was a child, so it is just within living memory.

Ponies were also employed in mines, and used during the war. Some fell ponies were crossed with the larger Clydesdale to produce the Dales, a larger pony more suitable for military use and pit work. Fast forward to the twenty-first century, and Fell ponies, an essential part of our Cumbrian heritage that have served people faithfully for generations, are sold at auction for 40 pounds. Considering that it is a legal requirement for them to have an equine passport that costs the breeder 50 pounds, this is heart breaking. Fell ponies are valueless and are often bought by safari parks to feed large animals.

I admire the Fell pony. I love its beauty, and its ability to live outside all year in the harshest of climates. I respect the important part that the pony has played in our history, and the mere sight of a semi-wild pony grazing on a fell is enough to bring me to tears.

I have been lucky enough to spend time with a breeder of a herd of fell ponies in the fells, feeding his ponies in winter. It is incomprehensible to me that these ponies are valueless, given what a sturdy riding pony they can be. The Queen and the Duke of Edinburgh both have Fell ponies. The Queen can be seen regularly riding out on her ponies, and the Duke of Edinburgh drives then with a carriage.

I was lucky enough to receive for my 40th birthday from my husband, the gift of my first Fell pony. Thankfully it was cheaper than a designer watch or a diamond!

I had my first pony, was now a semi-competent rider, and set out on the Cumbrian fells to celebrate. A weekend of riding was planned, which would circle Coniston Water and go over the Walna Scar road, and ancient packhorse route with a maximum altitude of 2000 feet, to the Duddon Valley. Despite the rain this was a fantastic weekend, and I was keen to enthuse others with the virtues of the stocky, sturdy pony, and enable other people to have adventures like this as well.

Our local riding centre had recently closed, due to a divorce, and the riding instructor was out of a job. Together we hatched a plan, a centre to promote the Cumbrian pony through open farm days, fell pony clubs for children and riding on old packhorse routes. After a battle to get planning permission for this, as we live in a designated 'quiet area' of the Lake District, we were ready to source our ponies and begin breaking them in.

We were determined that this was to be a long term project and investment, so our first purchases were Tom and

Rowan who were yearlings. Rowan was living with some Shire horses, and had white markings on his feet so was seen as undesirable. He had not been given much attention, and it took us three visits to be able to catch him and bring him here. We placed an advertisement asking for ponies, determined that we would use only registered ponies to support local breeders, and within a couple of days we had two replies.

Apple was living in North Yorkshire, and not being used. Like the first time I saw my husband at university, it was love at first sight, and we brought her home that day. She is a small, very stocky pony with a lot of feather (hair). I could gaze at her all day; she is absolute perfection to me. The cost of perfection? One thousand pounds. Compare that to the cost of a car and it is an absolute bargain, as we are talking about the equivalent of a top of the range Mercedes or BMW.

Apple does not, however, have the perfect temperament. I decided that I would break her in myself, and she twice threw me off in a fit of temper, once stamping on my leg and running off down the valley leaving me injured lying in the road. She was later brought back by a German motorcyclist, who declared she was 'a true sweetie'. I had a few other words for her, but such is the fell pony temperament. They are spirited and independent, and in her mind there was no doubt a very good reason why we were not going to cross the river that day.

The second pony was Susan. Susan belonged to an old lady and had been living in a barn all winter like a cow. She was grossly overweight, and filthy. As she came out of the barn and into the farmyard to see us she shook her mane, totally covering us in muck, and ran about shouting and kicking. This was not love at first sight for me. 'We'll have her,' said my friend. 'Are you sure?' I said, aghast. Whereas I had fallen in love with what appeared to me to be the perfect looking pony, my friend had fallen in love with a challenge.

We both had our favourites, and later that year we went head to head at Hawkshead Agricultural Show to settle the argument as to which was the better fell pony. Susan won the class, and Apple was second. For the entire duration of the show, Apple would not trot. 'Come another day,' said the judge 'If she behaves, she'll win.' Apple? Behave? No chance of that!

I bought thirteen fell ponies in total, all with different characters, and we worked together to break them in for the summer season. We also had to get our stables altered and rewired, as the public would be in there, and gather all the tack that was needed. It was a huge financial undertaking, with my husband and I providing the start up costs on the understanding that they would be repaid later from business takings.

The centre opened and was successful. We had plenty of bookings, and quite a bit of media coverage. We ran an open farm day where we demonstrated the versatility of the ponies by showing them in packsaddles and for riding. It was very well attended despite the rain.

All was going well, although there was a grumble of discontent from my friend about my children. As the centre was located at my house my children were constantly around, which was useful to me as they helped out with jobs, and I ultimately had the responsibility of looking after the ponies for seven days a week as they lived at my farm.

We then went on holiday for a week, which had been planned for months. My friend was left in charge of looking after the ponies, and some other friends were doing a brilliant job of house sitting. When we returned home my friend/business partner had cleared out her possessions. Despite being approximately £24,000 overdrawn at this point, she had no hesitation in changing jobs.

We dissolved the partnership, and she left the next day taking three ponies with her. My enduring feeling about this whole episode is that it is a missed opportunity to promote the fell pony. We had the best of intentions to promote the breed, and it all came to nothing.

Most of the ponies had to be sold to cover business costs, and my nearly new Defender was exchanged for a much older one, but I did manage to keep hold of Apple, Susan, Rowan and Tom.

The girls visited a superb stallion last summer, and as I write I am waiting for the pitter-patter of tiny fell pony hooves. I may not be able to educate people about the fell pony without my business partner who was the one with the equine qualifications, but I can breed them, and do my small bit in ensuring the future of the fell pony that way.

Champion Tup

'What are you doing with that Champion tup?'
Shouts Mum
'You've got someone else's sheep mixed in there'
But I haven't.
We are loading the sheep into the trailer
After the Westmorland show
And I have only green rosettes,
Fourth place,
Must try harder.

By swift negotiation
I have seized the opportunity
To buy the Champion tup
From a neighbouring pen,
And he's coming home with me.
'I'm glad you've more money than
You know what to do with'
Shouts Mum
As the sheep thunder past her and up the ramp.

'This is an investment,' I shout
'In our future,
Imagine the lambs.'
Half your flock
Is from your tup
Buy the best tup
You'll have the best lambs.
Dreaming of red rosettes next year
We head home with our bounty.

CHAMPION TUP

On Guy Fawkes's night the tup is released to the
ewes.

Raring to go and full of action
He pursues his ladies
In a bizarre courtship
Of curled lips and stamping feet.
When the ewe is ready she will let him near,
Until then she will skip off
Disinterested despite
His urgent show of affection.

A NATIVE BREED

Gradually he works his way through the flock,
Until Christmas time.
He has then finished his work for the year.
He is taken off to live in gentle pastures
With plenty of food
And a nice little shed to keep him dry.
Every indulgence is given to him
As we wait in anticipation of his
Prize winning lambs.

It's not a bad life to be a tup
Selected by physical excellence and beauty
They get to live out their lives
In a lush green paddock,
Once a year amongst the ewes for six weeks of feverish
activity
Then rest and relaxation,
Legs out, lying on grassy knoll.
I sometimes have to wake him to feed him
I only hope he is dreaming of red rosettes too.

North Ronaldsay Sheep
Sixteen North Ronaldsay ewes
One North Ronaldsay tup

It must be a wonderful thing to inherit an established farm where all the problem solving has been worked out over generations, and you have a basic template from which to work that has been tested through experience. I was starting from scratch when we moved here, keeping the native animals that interested me, and problem solving around them. Perhaps I should have started from the land, and worked around that. What fascinates me is the interaction between the native environment and the native animals, and how both benefit each other.

The remaining four fell ponies and the two miniature Shetland ponies were happily grazing in fifteen acres of rented land. The land is very undulating, with ancient anthills on steep sided valleys, areas of rushes and a river. There are large areas of gorse scrub, and brambles. There are small hills that the ponies can stand on top of to get a sense of perspective, and old oak trees to shelter underneath or to get shade. All in all, it is heaven for fell ponies. They have fun walking in the river and rolling on the hillsides.

There is ample food for them during the summer, with a variety of eating. The rushes are left alone during the summer, growing furiously. When the grass stops growing during the winter months the ponies turn to the rushes. They eat what must be about five acres of rushes over the winter, and require no additional feed. I was initially nervous about not feeding them, but one look at their constantly tubby tummies is all the reassurance needed. This is a very sustainable way of feeding them, and the land benefits from the rushes being eaten each year that will promote fresh new growth. Far from seeing the rushes as in inconvenience like most modern farmers, I see them as my crop of winter feed and as such are very valuable.

There was only one issue arising, and that was that the ponies do not eat some plants, especially ragwort. Ragwort is very poisonous to ponies, and must be uprooted. Once the ragwort had been uprooted, no small undertaking, something needed to be introduced to the field to eat up the excess plants.

Many sheep are praised for their conservation grazing

abilities, but in order to do the job properly they really need to be as primitive as possible. This is so they have not been conditioned over time to eating improved grass, and come to rely upon the kind of nutrition it provides.

The sheep that I decided upon were the fascinating North Ronaldsay. They come from the islands of North Ronaldsay and Linga Holm that are part of Orkney in Scotland. These sheep have lived there for generations, and have not been 'improved' like other breeds of sheep because of the remote location of the islands.

A project to preserve these sheep by the Rare Breeds Survival Trust involved taking some of the sheep off the island to protect their genetic heritage. If some catastrophe were subsequently to befall the sheep on the island, there would be small flocks elsewhere and the breed would not be lost. What makes these sheep even more remarkable is that they have survived on the island of North Ronaldsay despite not being highly prized by the islanders and banished from the grass on the island for most of the year. A huge wall was constructed around the island to prevent the sheep from getting to the best grazing which was reserved for cattle. The sheep survived by adapting their routines to fit in with the tides, and by eating seaweed.

They have had such a restricted diet it is important not to give the sheep too rich a diet. They cannot eat commercial sheep food, and some elements that they are not used to, such as copper, will poison them.

They live a thrifty life and were ideal for my cross-grazing project with the fell ponies. They have happily co-existed for three years now. They are hardy, but very flighty. They have no flocking instinct, and will scatter and run away very fast if they see a human or a dog approaching.

They lamb easily, and the lamb soon learns to run as fast as his/her mother. Unless you catch them on the first day of their life to check if they are a boy or a girl, you will have very little chance of catching them for several months until they become hungry in the winter and you can tempt them to come near you with a little sugar beet. I have succeeded in breeding these beautiful, uncatchable sheep and have sold tup lambs to buyers to cross with their hoggs for an easy first lambing.

North Ronaldsay are not a sheep to enjoy feeding and befriending, but they are an interesting conservation project for those interested in native breeds and conservation grazing. They are also a great sheep to take to an agricultural show as their horns are so impressive, a North Ronaldsay class will always have spectators.

Keeping North Ronaldsay sheep has also given me my first experience of selling sheep at auction. I had been to the auction several times buying sheep, and when you are selling breeding sheep you are expected to accompany your sheep into the ring. The ring is designed like a mini amphitheatre and all eyes are on you and your sheep from those sat in the seats looking down on you, or leaning on the bars at the ringside.

The first time I came through the double galvanised doors with my sheep I thought that I was going to faint. Thankfully my sheep began jumping about, and distracted me from the audience. Now when I wait in the pens to go into the sale ring I remind myself to breathe.

On my first auction the auctioneer came up to me and asked 'What instructions have you given your sheep?'

meaning 'Have you put a reserve price on your sheep?' I couldn't resist saying 'I've told them all to go out there and do their best and find a new home.' The look on the auctioneer's face said it all. Sheep are not a joking matter in Cumbria, and I should have known better.

Brief Encounter

Neighbour, 74, no relations
Passing in Land Rover
Bull in trailer
Pulls over

'I would love to stay and work with you lassie'
Says he 'but I'm feeling a bit old nowadays.
Should something happen to me
Will you mind me cows?'

Full of emotion
We hug in our overalls
Both stink of silage and have mud on our faces
Ankle deep in sticky muck.

'I'll mind your cows,' I promise
And he drives off
With some sort of contentment
Much unsaid.

BRIEF ENCOUNTER

'I don't like to go off site' he says
Meaning he never leaves his farm
From one year to the next
But should something happen to him

What would happen to the cows?
What would happen to the farm?
What changes would happen here
Now that neighbour, 74, has gone off site for
good?

Dexter Cattle
Suckler herd of seven cows and calves

When I was ten and showing an interest in farming and animals, my parents bought me a calf for my birthday. The calf cost £15 and my uncle would fatten the calf and sell it on. In the meantime I could enjoy its rough tongue licking me, and touching its wet nose.

At the end of the year when the calf was sold, my uncle sent me a cheque in the post. Minus the cost of the feed, the calf had sold for £15. I was quite astonished, but it was an interesting lesson in hill farming. It is certainly something you should not do for financial gain!

Hill farmers have traditionally kept a mixture of cattle and sheep. In my own home we have three partitions where the dairy cows would have been milked. Some farms have retained dairy herds in the Lake District despite the poor price paid for milk, others have a suckler herd of beef cattle.

I felt that I needed to improve my skills with cattle before we got some cows of our own. I asked a neighbour with a dairy herd if I could help out for two days a week. He had a group of 20 young female cows in a barn near my house. These were being kept for a customer, and would become her milking cows. It was very important that the cows were docile, and used to being around people. They were tethered at the neck in stalls. They wore a rope collar with a toggle, and the collar was attached to the side of the stall. They could stand, sit and lie comfortably, but could not wander around inside the barn.

Some people do not like to see cows tethered in barns, but these cows never showed a moment's unhappiness or illness the whole time that I spent with them. They became very used to people feeding them by hand, walking behind them and to the side of them, and touching them and talking to them. I think the fact that there were two cows to each stall helped. The cows were warm and happy in each other's company.

The first week that the cows came inside they were very nervous of people. I pass by the barns several times a day, and would pop in to see how they were. The barn is a traditional Lake District bank barn and there are hundreds of similar barns in the Lake District. They are set into the hill, the cow stalls are underneath with their doors and windows at the front of the building, and there is a drive around the back of the barn where previously a horse and cart, and now a tractor, can drive up and store hay in through some double doors onto the loft space above the byre. The hay keeps lovely and dry from the body heat of the cows underneath during the winter. There is a little ladder and a hatchway from the cows to the hay, so that the farmer can climb up and throw hay down to his animals.

There is a walkway down the middle of the barn, with ten cows on each side. The first day that I went in to see the cows two panicked. One got herself stuck with her front legs over the partition into the walkway, and the second with her legs up on a windowsill. Both were trying to escape from me.

Gradually over the next few weeks these cows came to trust me, and listen out for me passing. I only had to open my door on a Monday or Tuesday, my days for feeding the cows, and the mooing would start. The girls knew that I was coming. They can clearly count the days of the week! This is how dairy farmers have built up relationships with their cattle for hundreds of years. By the time the cows left to go to their new owners there was complete trust between the cows and myself.

This trust was put to the test when my neighbour had, for some reason, untied some of the cows within the barn and left the door open by mistake. The cows bolted out onto the road in the sunshine, just as I was passing by.

'Don't worry, I'll call them back in.'

'Who do you think you are, a cow whisperer or something?'

Five minutes later and the cows were secured back in the barn. It's a wonderful thing when there is trust between people and animals.

Farming is often thought of as a solitary occupation. There is always time to think, but there is always time to help a neighbour, lend or borrow a piece of equipment, or have a chat. We live together in a remote area, and we all get along out of necessity. If a tree falls down blocking a road we all work together to clear the road. If our water supply is frozen a neighbour will help us carry milk churns of water from the river.

We have a 'perfect republic of shepherds' as Wordsworth said, in which we are all equal. How do you become part of this republic as a newcomer to the area? Family connections can help, on meeting people for the first time who are connected with farming I mention my uncle. Once people can place me in the cultural jigsaw of Cumbria it is easier to be accepted. Accepted, but it will take a couple more generations in this valley before we are thought of as local I suspect.

I have been laughed at for bidding against myself at auction (not true, I am not that daft), for my choice of sheep and my liking of ponies, but I have also been complimented on my strong lambs. I am getting there, slowly.

My neighbour and I enjoyed the 'crack' working together in the cow barn, and I learnt a lot about cows. We also had a few laughs along the way. The lights at the back of the cow barn didn't work. When I asked him why he said, 'Bloody electric's expensive' so I bought a huge pack of energy saving light bulbs. When I was about to replace the light bulbs he said

'No, FIXING the bloody electric's expensive' and swung his fork up to the conduit by way of illustration. There was an enormous bang and a flash, and all the lights went out. After this apprenticeship – I must have been the oldest farm apprentice in the history of the valley – I felt ready to get my own cows.

We decided to get Dexter cattle. This is again a traditional native breed, and I thought they would suit the land that we had. They would cross graze with some Hebridean sheep. A new handling area had to be built to allow us to trap and handle the cows in a 'crush', and we had to have several TB tests as a new herd. This was worrying as the cattle are near a large badger sett, but thankfully all the tests have been TB free.

We bought seven registered Dexter cattle, and they visited a neighbour's bull. I decided to keep the cattle outside all year. It seems natural to me that animals are outdoors, and I will only buy or breed animals that are hardy enough to live outdoors all year here.

The cattle are excellent foragers. They enjoy a wide variety of eating from their browsing and grazing. They particularly love crab apples, and will stand under a crab apple tree waiting for them to fall in the autumn, pushing the tree backwards and forwards in order to speed the process up. It is said that the seeds of a crab apple tree cannot germinate unless they have passed through the body of a cow.

In the winter, however, there is not enough for the cattle to eat. They need extra nourishment in the form of hay or silage. The fields here can totally provide for the nutritional needs of the cattle, they are sustainable, but only if the summer crop of hay or silage is cut and kept for them.

It is a careful balancing act deciding where to feed the cows in winter, as the land will inevitably get poached (churned up) in feeding areas. At the moment I am rotating the areas that we use for feeding. It is all a big jigsaw puzzle being worked out. Sometimes the pieces don't quite fit together as you would expect them to. The animals' interaction with the land, and their dependence on it, must also be balanced with environmental schemes. Anyone who has the idea that farming is a simple, unchallenging job with a kind of 'groundhog' existence is far from the reality. It is the most challenging thing that I have ever attempted to do. The status quo is constantly shifting with weather conditions, seasonal changes, medical emergencies, new animals and government schemes and incentives alongside changing legislation. There is honestly never a dull moment.

The Dexters proved very easy to look after when they were not in calf, and once they were ready to go to the bull we arranged for them to go to a pedigree Dexter bull. They stayed there for three cycles of 22 days, and then were delivered home, hopefully pregnant.

They ate silage and a little food over the winter. The silage was our own silage that a contractor had made for us. It was analysed by a feed merchant, who then worked out a detailed feeding programme for me. The cattle were easy enough to manage; each day they followed me over to their feeding area. One of the cows was very slow, and lagged behind the others. She was the oldest cow, and I said to myself that this would be her last winter. Hopefully she would have a lovely heifer calf to replace her, as her temperament was ideal.

Hector usually fed the cows before school, and one

morning he said, 'One of them hasn't come over for food. She won't move away from the fence in the corner.'

As soon as the school bus had gone I went over to investigate. The reason that she wouldn't move away from the fence was that there was a tiny, perfect calf stuck on the other side of the fence. I thought she must have somehow given birth over the top of the fence.

Seeing an opportunity to ear tag the calf while it was stuck, I raced home and got my ear tags and pliers. Calves have to be ear tagged within 30 days of birth legally, but I figured that like lambs they would be easier to ear tag on the first day while they were still sleepy. The calf was stuck in some brambles, and I had freed it from the brambles before racing off, however when I came back with the ear tags the calf was happily having a drink from its mother. I have no idea how it got through.

When it had finished drinking I cautiously approached the calf. The cow had no problem with me touching it, and I ear tagged the calf and checked it's underneath parts. It was a heifer calf, a little girl. I was elated. I sat on the ground next to the calf and the cow. All of us felt very pleased with ourselves. I picked the calf up again several times. Never having had a calf on the farm before I wanted to feel the weight of the calf, and I kept reassuring myself that it was female.

The calf was registered with the Dexter Cattle Society as Lakedistrict Bluebell (bluebells being out in the hedgerow she was born in, on the wrong side of the fence!) The birth was reported to the British Cattle Movement service.

So far so good. We were pretty elated with our first calf

and waiting for the second. In the midst of this, one of our neighbours had a TB scare on some rented land. As I understand it, the farm that is about three miles from us, had rented some land near to the auction at Junction 36 on the M6. Cattle were sometimes put on this land while they were fattened up. These cattle had not been within 20 miles of our land, but because they are linked to a neighbouring farm, we all had to have TB tests in the valley.

Our TB test was scheduled for the next day, and on the telephone the receptionist at the vets had made a comment about making sure that all the cows had two ear tags in, so that was on my mind. We were checking the cows before going to pick up my youngest son from a club at school. Hector had just returned from his last GCSE exam, so was in a buoyant mood at the thought of never having to go back to school. We found that one of the cows had had another calf. We dashed home for the ear tags, determined to quickly tag the calf before going to school.

This was the first time that this cow had calved, and she had hidden the calf in some bracken. My son and I approached the calf. I held her (another girl) while Hector got the ear tags ready. At this point the calf let out a little noise, and the cow started to get anxious, pacing towards us.

'Let's leave her,' said Hector

'We're here now, we may as well just do it quickly' I said, and held my shepherds crook up to the cow to show her that she should not come near us. At this point the calf again let out a little moan, and while I am rather hazy on the details, I do remember the cow pushing past Hector, barging him out of the way, and knocking me onto the ground. I let go of the calf and said 'It's ok, it's ok.'

But the cow had totally lost control. She had me on the floor between a crag and a fence, and was jumping on my head. She was determined to kill me, and Hector could only stand and watch. She would do a few jumps on my head and then pause. I was sure that my skull must be broken, and knew that my forehead had split open from banging into a rock on the ground. While the cow paused Hector shouted 'NOW' and somehow with the super strength that adrenalin provides he lifted me over the fence. We were both out of the field, but I was badly injured, lying on the road with my head bleeding profusely, trying to remain conscious. I was aware of a puddle of blood growing on the road next to my head.

I had a phone in my pocket but there was no mobile signal. I was very aware that if we dialled 999 from our remote location the air ambulance would be sent, at great cost. I told Hector not to phone 999 as an ambulance could not reach us down the tiny lane, and would take too long to get here, and I didn't want the air ambulance called at a cost of thousands of pounds.

Hector ran home but Antony had gone out fell running. Oscar had passed his driving test the day before this happened, so he went to start the car. The radio had been left on and the battery was flat; what a catalogue of disaster.

The boys raced to find a neighbour. They found Helen, who kindly abandoned cooking her husband a roast dinner and drove up to where I was lying, in her brand new Volvo. The boys had brought some tea towels to act as makeshift bandages, but even with these tied around my head I was aware that the blood was gushing all over her pristine car.

Helen had been on a 'speed awareness' course that afternoon, and after attending that drove in a very controlled way to Accident and Emergency. The whole event was quite comical. I kept nodding off in the front of the car, and Oscar kept pulling my head up by my hair to bring me upright again, and Hector acted as adviser to Helen about the speed limits. We telephoned ahead and someone was waiting for us with a wheelchair at the hospital when we got there. Soon I was tucked up in bed with a drip feeding me pain relief and feeling in safe hands.

The hospital at Barrow in Furness has sometimes received rather a lot of bad press, but the care I received there was exceptional. Nobody ever asked why I had got myself into such a dangerous situation, or criticized my actions. The ladies who looked after me had plenty of time for me, were always kind and never in a hurry.

A CT scan revealed that there were, remarkably, no broken bones or serious injuries. We couldn't believe it; my son told me later that he was absolutely certain that I was going to die. I am very grateful that it was me and not him that was attacked. It would have been horrific to watch your child being injured like that, I would much rather have the injuries myself, especially as he had wisely said that we should not tag the calf.

Hector was much more aware of the animal's mood than I was. I was intent on getting the job done. I have learnt a lesson, never handle a calf without its mother being properly restrained, and be aware of the animal's moods at all times.

Lying on the floor it did cross my mind that I might be about to die. I have never been afraid of dying, and if that was my allotted time to die, so be it. I could see Hector's boots as I was lying on the floor, and I remember thinking that if I die I hope he doesn't blame himself for being so keen on getting cows, as none of this is his fault.

The recovery was painful but successful. The nurses stitched down both sides of my face and down from my forehead to my eyebrow. My eyebrow itself was sewn back together. Down the back of my head was stapled in long tramlines as it was out of view tucked behind my hair. This was the most painful experience of my life, worse than the labours having my boys and the stitches afterwards. When the nurses had finished stapling my head I said, 'How do the staples come out?' 'Ah' said the nurse 'we were wondering when you would ask that.' Having them removed was also painful.

I came out of hospital ready to sell all of the cows. I could not take the risk of them injuring my children. The first job was to get rid of the offending cow. Thankfully a neighbour offered to take her, knowing her history. In the days following the attack we also had to have the TB test before the cow could be moved, which was postponed because of the accident. A neighbour came to help Hector get all the cows into the crush. When they were all contained in the pen I got out of the Land Rover to see what was happening. As soon as the cow that had attacked me saw me she started shaking her head. My neighbour shouted 'Get back in the car NOW,' worried that she would lose her self control again.

I am still very cautious around cows, and will never attempt to do anything again without having them properly restrained and certainly not on my own. Farming can be very dangerous, but hopefully we learn from our mistakes and do not repeat them. This was certainly an experience that I have no desire to repeat.

It was not a successful year in terms of calving. After the first heifer calf, the second heifer calf went with her mother who was sold after the attack. One of the other cows had a bull calf, but the rest including my beautiful old cow, did not calve. The old cow that was clearly not going to survive another winter here was sold to a farm with warmer climes, and the rest went off to the bull again. Hopefully future years will be more successful, but at the moment our outgoings for the cows are clearly more than our incomings. Difficult business this hill farming. Difficult indeed.

From a Mother to a Son

We are part of this valley
You and I
We made the landscape
And the landscape made us.

Our ancestors cleared the forest
And we keep it as it is.
We build up fallen walls
And we tend the animals that keep it green.

When we gan yam at night
Someone's grandfather's grandfather
Made this house for us
By clearing stones.

Building it into the hill for shelter
Some 500 years ago.
Remember when your friend once asked
'Is this the olden days?'

Not many families have to collect and chop wood
To keep the kitchen warm in winter.
Most would refuse to bring water from the stream
And boil it up on the open fire to wash.

Folks in towns and cities
Have lost the connection with the land.
I know because I've tried it,
And so will you, most likely.

Will you return
To chop the wood,
Light the stove and
Lift the pans?

We are part of this valley
You and I,
And when I'm tired of keeping on
Will you keep it on for me?

Shearing sheep, photograph by Fergus Meanwell

Border Collies

The kind of traditional livestock farming that most of us practice in the Lake District is often referred to as 'stick and dog' farming. It is a traditional way of working on 'Shank's pony' aided by a stick and a dog. The stick can be easily bought from any farm supply shop, and the use of it mastered within an afternoon. The dog, however, is much more difficult to acquire and much more difficult to master.

We decided that in order to gather our sheep more easily we would need to get a sheepdog to help with our growing flock. Up until this point we had relied upon the sheep following us with a bucket of food into a confined area, then shutting them in with a collection of hurdles. Some sheep, usually the older ones, know what is in the bucket and are easy to catch. Other sheep do not understand the routine and evade capture.

There would be no point in buying a puppy, as we had no idea how to train it, so we were on the look out for an older dog that fancied an early retirement by moving from a big farm to a small farm. Dogs like this are very hard to find, working dogs usually deteriorate rapidly in health when they are older, and die without enjoying a period of retirement. Farm dogs live relatively short lives punctuated by challenging days of high activity. After this outdoor life they tend to fade rapidly and die quickly.

The other option was to buy a trained dog. Unfortunately most trained sheep dogs would be way out of our price range, costing several thousand pounds. We began to make enquiries, and like with the sheep, several dogs were brought to our attention. Whenever you are looking to buy something, there is usually somebody looking to sell you it. An ex-trials dog was suggested to us, via a complicated series of messages being passed from person to person. Sheep dog trials are a long established sport requiring a high level of commitment from both the owner and the dog. We found ourselves in a field on the outskirts of Barrow-in-Furness one evening, with the owner of the dog we had gone to meet telling us 'I've lost my home, wife and children to sheepdog trials.' Not the conversation opener that you expect!

He had been training a young dog called Bob, and had become frustrated with him. Bob didn't like the tannoy at events, and also only liked to round up sheep from the left. He said that Bob 'just wanted to be loved.'

He took Bob into a field with sheep in it to show us that he could round them up, and then said that he had too many dogs, Bob was surplus to requirements, and was for sale for £100. If we took him today we would not be able to return him. He assured us that Bob had never bitten or shown any aggressive tendencies, so we decided to take him. At best we would have gained a useful sheepdog, at worst we would have gained a pet dog.

The owner was right; Bob did just want to be loved. He was keen to please and quickly came to trust me. I walked him on a long lead at first, and then let him off. He trusted me completely and I found I could control him by 'eye'.

We would make eye contact and he would go away or come back, as required.

Bob's previous owner had said that given his nervousness around loud noises, he would be happier with another dog to work with and recommended that we get a puppy. We didn't need to be persuaded to get a puppy, and began to look. I wanted a female puppy, as two males might not get on, and she proved quite challenging to find.

Eventually we saw an advert for collie puppies in Colne, Lancashire. They had been bred from trials dogs. We went to see them one day after a Winter League fell race. Whilst the fell race was on, in Sedbergh, it began to snow. As we drove into Lancashire the snow began to come thick and fast. I began to get worried that we would not be able to get home, and it was going to have to be a five-minute decision about whether or not to take the puppy. The puppies were located in a remote valley that was rapidly filling up with snow.

The puppy, of course, was adorable and soon we were heading home with her in the back of the Defender through thick snow. We called the puppy Moss, and she was a Christmas present from my grandad. From the beginning Moss formed a great bond with me, and became a good friend. When you are with your dogs and no other humans all day they do become your friends and companions. They become someone to work with, and talk to.

We took Moss to sheepdog training, and whilst she managed to round up sheep, she was what the trainer called 'sticky', meaning that she lacked enthusiasm. She would work for a short time and then seemed to think 'job done' and sit down. She became very adept at 'holding up' a stray sheep. With our rare breed sheep that are   escapologists this is a very useful skill. She could find and 'hold up' an escaped sheep in a wood. Then she would bark to let me know where she was. She could also 'hold up' an individual sheep in a field, once I had pointed it out to her with my stick.

She has not yet mastered the ability to gather and move sheep. We still did not have what we would consider to be a really useful dog. Fergus wanted to have his own dog, both Bob and Moss being definitely my dogs and looking to me for instruction all the time. We saw some puppies advertised at a farm on the side of a mountain called Black Coombe and went to choose one. He chose a black, tri-coloured bitch puppy as his eleventh birthday present.

If you have the time and the space a puppy has to be an excellent present for an outdoor loving boy. The following year he received sheepdog training lessons for his birthday present and the pair of them learnt together how to move sheep. There is something very thrilling about communicating on a hillside with your dog to move sheep.

The first stage of training involved Fergus's dog Pegg being on a long rope moving around the sheep, with a piece of alkathene pipe move her away from the sheep if she tried to bite them. To stop her he stood on the rope. It is a natural instinct for border collies to chase and round up sheep as they flock together. Most sheep will flock together for safety when they perceive there is the threat of a predator approaching.

The dog must learn not to bite the sheep, and to respond to the directions that the shepherd is giving. These directions are taught by letting the dog naturally move around the sheep, and matching the command to the action. For example, when the dog stops or lies down the shepherd says, 'lie down, lie down, lie down' until she gets up. The dog then begins to associate the command 'lie down' with resting, and in time will lie down on command.

The dog must overcome her natural instinct to chase the sheep, and usually her desire to please and work with the shepherd is strong enough to overcome her desire to chase sheep.

Fergus and Pegg were working together well, and by the time she was eighteen months old she was a very helpful dog. Jobs became much easier at home with a dog that was keen enough to rely upon. During the day Pegg was

on a long chain in the stables, with the door open so that she could wander inside or outside as the mood took her. She had various places that she liked to rest, one of which being an old bread crate. One morning I went in to sweep out the stables, having already walked and fed the dogs, when I noticed Pegg snuggled right into the bread crate, with a small squeaky noise coming from the crate. I could see something moving, and I thought 'Oh my goodness she has caught a swallow'. Swallows are summer visitors to our stables, and as they swoop in and out the dogs are always trying unsuccessfully to catch them.

Closer inspection revealed that it was not a swallow, but two tiny puppies that Pegg was looking after. For two years I had been hoping that Moss would have puppies, and had allowed her to share a loose box in the stables with Bob, and now unexpectedly Pegg had produced two perfect puppies. Both were black and white, one boy and one girl. I rushed into the house to find something more suitable than a bread crate for her whelping box. Oscar had recently left for university, leaving some solid wood bookshelves that were no longer required. I took the interior shelves off, leaving a large wooden frame with a wooden floor, and carried it outside.

Old towels were put into the box, and Pegg settled in there with the two puppies, unchained now as I was certain that she would not wander off and leave the puppies. When I came back from picking up Fergus from school he ran excitedly into the stables and shouted 'Mum, its not two, its four.' She had had two more female puppies, both tri-coloured.

There followed eight weeks of joy, as Fergus and I

looked after the puppies together, fascinated with their development. They were weighed every evening, and their weights recorded on a blackboard.

We looked online for people advertising that they wanted a puppy, and took deposits for two immediately. The remaining two were advertised online and sold within a week. At last we had succeeded in producing something that people were falling over themselves to buy.

We decided that we would not keep any of the puppies ourselves, as we did not really need another dog at this point, and whilst it would be tempting it was better to sell the puppies and invest the money in our existing dogs.

With the money from the puppies we managed to build a proper kennel area so that the dogs didn't have to live in the stables chained up. They each got a kennel and run, so that they could go indoors or outdoors at will, and live separately so that there would not be any more unplanned pregnancies.

I do expect to have more planned pregnancies, as the whole experience was so enjoyable. It was very satisfying to find dogs for people who had been searching for them, and to know that the dogs had gone to good homes where they would be valued. It just shows, on a hill farm you never know what is going to happen next.

Hay Time

Hay time in the 1970s,
Anxiously watching the weather forecast,
Will we get a week of dry weather?
Will we get the hay in?
The whole summer holiday
Was occupied by anxiety
About hay.

Then came silage wraps
Or silage clamps.
The anxiety was taken away,
We knew we had winter feed.
The bad weather didn't matter,
And hay time, with hay time teas,
Was forgotten.

Then last year
Unexpectedly
We had a fantastic summer.
Glorious weather
Day after day
And the talk turned to
Making hay.

A NATIVE BREED

Long forgotten bailers
Were dragged from barns,
Former hay barns
Stacked to the brim with
Farming detritus.
Old machinery was fettled up
And ready to go.

For two glorious weeks
Hay was made again
In this valley.
Spun, bailed, thrown
On the trailer.
I watched the trailer
Moving across the field.

My three boys
Bare-chested in the sun
Throwing and stacking bales,
Then climbing on the stack
As the trailer was pulled
Painfully slowly uphill
With them lying on the top.

I am tearful at the sight
Of my sundrenched children
Riding on the hay bales.
I hadn't realised
How much it meant to me
They had, for once,
Made hay.

The Hay Meadow
5.5 Acres

Hay meadow photograph Fergus Meanwell.

When I started keeping animals I bought the hay required from a friend. He had worked on the renovation of our property, and mentioned that he had been asked to make hay from his elderly grandad's hay meadow locally.

Since we moved to Rusland I have been lucky enough to work part-time occasionally for Cumbria Wildlife Trust as a wildlife tutor. Depending on which projects are on-going at the time, this work includes educating people about wildlife in Cumbria. One project that I was asked to work on was the hay meadow project. This was a lottery-funded project to educate people about the value of hay meadows, and to encourage farmers to consider making hay rather than silage. Hay meadows are valued for their wildlife; centuries of grazing and mowing for hay have created meadows in Cumbria with a profusion of wild flowers.

Only about 1,000 hectares of traditional hay meadow are left in England, and 100 hectares in Scotland. Cumbria is thought to have around ten per cent of these English meadows, where a combination of small inaccessible fields and farmers without the money to buy large machinery has ensured their survival. Throughout the rest of England a lot of hay meadows have been lost as they have been repeatedly cut for silage and fertilized. If the grass is cut before the flowers have had time to set their seeds each year, they will not grow in the meadows any more.

Making silage has become an invaluable way of managing livestock for many farmers in the UK. Silage is wrapped and the grass does not have to be dry when it is cut and baled. This takes away the traditional summertime anxiety that farmers have about whether they are going to get a whole week of hot, dry weather to make hay. In Cumbria this can be particularly tricky. If farmers could not make hay because of bad weather their whole existence could be jeopardised, as there would be no alternative way of feeding their stock before the advent of silage.

Silage in bales, wrapped and stacked, is an easy way of ensuring that the farmers have enough to feed their animals for the winter, and the majority of farmers have stopped making hay.

Making hay does have benefits to both the environment

and to the animals eating it. A bale of hay will provide a whole variety of plants, some of which will be beneficial for different ailments that the animals may get over winter. Eating a variety of plants is good for animals, like we eat a variety of foods to keep healthy. A square metre of traditional hay meadow will have up to 50 different plant species growing in it.

The flowers need to set seed for the following year before they are cut, and the long grass in the fields has benefits for wildlife. The grass provides protection for mammals that live under its shelter hiding from predators, as well as snakes and reptiles. We have adders, slow worms, toads and newts on our land.

The flowers attract insects to the field, and they in turn attract insect eating birds. Birds also like to eat the hay seeds that fall from the hay racks in winter as the sheep eat them, and will even sit on sheep's backs and pick out the hay seeds that are stuck in the fleece.

The work with the Wildlife Trust made me understand how valuable hay meadows are for the environment. Previously I had been guilty of thinking about only the end product, the hay itself. I was convinced that I would like to manage my own meadow, and thrilled when we purchased one.

The hay meadow that we bought is at an elevation of 200m above sea level, so qualifies as an upland hay meadow. It had been fertilized in recent years, and had lost some of its floral diversity, but some plants did remain.

During the first year of flowering I observed pignut, knapweed, great burnet, sorrel and red clover. I would like to introduce more species, so with advice from Cumbria

Wildlife Trust I am adding plug plants into some areas around the meadow that will not be grazed this year. Hopefully the seeds from these plants will trample by the sheep that graze the meadow in winter throughout the whole field. The meadow was grazed throughout the first winter. As well as spreading seeds, sheep on the meadow will also help to fertilize the land, and seeds from the hay that is being fed to the sheep will keep reseeding the meadow.

At the end of May, rather late, the sheep were moved off the meadow and the grass allowed to grow. It grew very slowly at first, but by the end of June there had been considerable growth. A new building to store the bales of hay was being constructed for us by a neighbour, and the building was not finished until 26 July. I asked the neighbour who had offered to cut and bale the hay for us to cut it as soon as possible, the end of the first week in July is usually considered the best time to cut the hay, so we were running a little late.

The weather now broke, and we had rain for days. Each time we phoned the neighbour to enquire about whether he thought the weather was going to be good enough to cut the hay he asked us if we wanted big bales of silage. No, we would hold our nerve and hope for haymaking weather.

Eventually on 11 August the grass was cut. There was still some uncertainty about whether the week would be warm enough to dry the hay. As soon as the grass was cut the heavens opened, and we stood and watched as our grass got wetter and wetter. We were told not to be disappointed if we made silage. I was unable to sleep, lying awake waiting for drops of rain to fall on the velux windows signalling the end of my haymaking dream.

The rain did not come, and by the 13 August the grass was considered dry enough to bale. It was all hands on deck. When I arrived at the meadow hay making was well under way. It was oppressively hot. One tractor was going around rowing up the hay, and another was baling it. My job was to move the completed bales into groups of nine for a tractor to pick up altogether. It was hot, heavy work. Some of the bales were relatively easy to lift, but some where the grass was thicker were very heavy. I could only just lift them. My neighbour saw me struggling to lift them and set his baler so that they were not so heavy. I needed bales that I could carry in winter by myself so the weight was crucial.

The bales were then taken over to the barn where my son stacked them. Before the rain came we had made and stacked 350 bales of hay in a morning. It was very satisfying to see our own hay safely stored in our own barn. A step nearer to a sustainable, self-sufficient farm. If we repair some stone walls so that another field can be given over to hay during the summer months – at the moment the sheep can get into it through wall gaps – we should have enough hay to feed our animals for the year without having to buy in extra food. We will also be providing a home for insects, mammals, reptiles, amphibians and birds. Best of all, we will be producing a top quality food for our animals.

My son is also searching for a vintage tractor and hay making equipment so that he can make the hay himself. We were all exhausted by both the anxiety of when we could make hay, and the physicality of actually making the hay, but as we lay on top of the hay bales in the hay barn, absolutely shattered, it had been worth it. The elation of having made your own hay and the resulting exhaustion is something everyone should experience once in a lifetime.

Lying on the hay bales looking out at the mountains I somehow feel connected to all the farmers who came before me and made hay in these meadows. The Lake District is a working landscape, it's also a work in progress. The hay that fills the barns in years to come will be seeded from these bales that I am lying on, so I am also connected to all the farmers who will follow me to make hay on this land. They will feel the exhaustion, and the exhilaration looking at the view on a summer's afternoon. Long may it continue, it's part of what makes us Cumbrian and connects us to this landscape.

Windy Day on the Fells

Native sheep
Back to the wind
Face to the wall
Lying low, resting.

Native pony
Back to the wind
Face to the wall
Lying low, resting.

Westmerian farmer
Face to the wind
Up against the wall
Forgotten but keeping on.

The Lake District Farmer

Several of the native species in this book have been endangered and brought back from the brink of extinction. There is one native species that is vital to the survival of the rest, and it is often overlooked. This is the Lake District shepherd, shepherdess or farmer, the guardian of the land and the animals. This is the builder of stone walls and the layer of hedges, the unblocker of culverts and remover of fallen trees. Often the silent, seemingly invisible worker in the landscape. What qualities does such a farmer need?

First and foremost the farmer needs to be a worker. There is work to be done 365 days of the year. The farmer must be able to accept that the work will never be complete. There will always be jobs to do, and there will never be a point at which your work is finished. If I was to work every day for the rest of my life on our small farm, I don't think I would ever have all the walls entirely mended and all the hedges laid. The upside of this is that you are never bored. You never wake up with the day stretching ahead of you, and wonder what to do. You always wake up with a great long list of jobs to do, and the time when it will go dark and you will have to stop working outside ticking towards you.

As well as working every day, you have to be content in your surroundings. You will spend most of your life within a couple of miles of your home, so this is not a job

for those who like to travel. I used to love exploring new places, but now I am perfectly content with observing seasonal changes on my land and acting accordingly. I have no need to travel or go anywhere else, because my whole world is enclosed within my farm.

I begin to feel anxious if I am away from home for too long, as a neighbour once said to me 'I don't like to go off site.' This is quite a significant change in outlook that has come over me since we moved to this farm. I enjoy seeing the mountains from my farm each day but I no longer feel the need or desire to go up them. There is enough to occupy both my mind and my body on the farm.

As an independent fell farmer you are dependant on nobody, and nobody is dependant on you. There is no complicated hierarchy of human resources. You make all decisions. All mistakes made are your own, and you are responsible for them. Often, unless you catch a friend passing on a quad bike, there is no second opinion and you are literally on your own making life and death decisions. This is one of the aspects of farming that I like best, the autonomy of it.

You do need the ability to get on with your neighbours and work as a team to gather sheep from a common or make hay. There are times of the year when you will need to work together and these cannot always be planned in advance. There may be a flood, a fallen tree blocking a road, or snow to clear, and the valley will work together to get the job done. Expensive equipment is sometimes shared, or hired collaboratively, but for most of the year you will be on your own, making decisions and solving problems.

There is often said to be a 'crisis in hill farming' as many older farmers do not have heirs to take on their farms. The crisis I have observed has not been a lack of people wanting to farm, but that there are not enough traditional farms for people to take over. Farmers do not generally retire; they keep on working as they have done for as long as they can. They will 'keep a few sheep for a hobby', a hobby which consumes most of their working day.

The crisis in the Lake District comes from the desirability of the land; so that when farms are sold young entrants to farming cannot afford them. They are often bought by people as holiday residences, or split into several small parcels of land and sold off. It is not unheard of for land to sell for £30,000 per acre in small parcels. People will buy a small piece of the Lake District for a private campsite, or to avoid inheritance tax. There may be an opportunity to rent these fields back, but not usually on a long tenancy agreement.

Some farms are let as tenant farms, the National Trust has a large number of these in the Lake District. I have tried to obtain a National Trust tenancy myself. First of all I went on a hill farming course sponsored by the National Trust at Newton Rigg College, then went through an application procedure with them, for a farm that was not really available to rent. I then applied for a National Trust tenancy, but the competition was intense. The situation is not helped when the National Trust sell off some of their farms, such as Low Longmire in the Rusland Valley. The crisis in hill farming is a crisis of opportunity for people to become hill farmers; it is difficult to see how this is going to change. Perhaps the World Heritage bid for the cultural heritage of the Lake District may go some way towards valuing farmers more.

Government policy and landowners interest in re-wilding also chip away at the opportunities to farm a hill farm, as fewer sheep on the fells will support fewer shepherds and their families. What is more important, the physical geography or the landscape here that many know and love and the people that created it and maintain it? The landscape as we see it and the farmers who created and maintain it cannot be detached from each other. It is the farmer who has made and steadily maintains the landscape that we love with its green fields, stone walls and laid hedges, with animals peacefully grazing.

If the land was re-wilded, and the farmer cannot farm, who would maintain the walls and the hedges? I cannot see that an overgrown Lake District with fallen down walls and overgrown fields would be an attractive place to visit. It needs people to maintain it, and at the moment there is a small army of fell farmers who are doing all of this work for virtually no economic gain, as they simply love their job. They are not farming for financial gain; they are farming because they are hill farmers.

The farmer, in the face of bad weather, sickness, injury, government policy, academics disputing his value in broadsheet newspapers, carries stoically on. It is his very 'stickability' that defines him. His ability to keep on keeping on, hat pulled over his ears against the wind. He is a stubborn, hardy, native breed like the animals he tends. He too is worthy of protection like those native animals, although I do not believe he is endangered. Some people would have you believe that all the great farming characters of the Lake District are gone. They are not, we're still making them, don't worry.

There is also a surprising amount of paperwork to be done on the farm, some of which can now be done online. An agent can do applications for schemes such as countryside stewardship, but the farmer must be capable of maintaining his holding register and completing documentation when moving animals. There are two main ways in which farmers are paid by the government for taking care of the land. The first is the Basic Payment Scheme, by which farmers are paid a certain amount per hectare for keeping the land in good condition and observing the rules of 'cross compliance' (for example, when to cut or lay hedges during the year etc). The second is Countryside Stewardship, where the farmer can get additional money for looking after the land in an environmentally friendly way. These schemes are competitive, and just because you apply for them does not mean that you will get the go ahead.

People seem to think that farmers are awash with money, and begrudge them this 'subsidy'. I do not think of it as a subsidy, but as a payment for keeping the land in good condition. The average income of a hill farmer is thought to be round £8,000 per year. To earn that £8,000 he will have worked around twelve hours a day, 365 days a year. Here in the Lake District he will have been working to maintain the landscape that thousands of people come to see each year. Surely we cannot begrudge him that £8,000.

Hill farming is unlikely to make you rich, but it might just keep you interested in life and content with it. One Monday morning I was walking up the hill to the cow barns and my neighbour was waiting for me, leaning on his muck fork

'I'm just wondering,' he shouts as I walk up the hill 'if you'll be coming up that hill in ten years time to do cows, and if I'll still be here in ten years time.'

'Probably' I shout back. It's a small answer to a big question, but we both know that there is nowhere else that we would rather be than here in the valley, looking after our animals.

Being outside in all weathers, observing seasonal changes, you almost become part of the landscape yourself. You have the privilege of observing wildlife from dawn to dusk, and sometimes you just have to stop and drink in the view.

It is late September, the end of the shepherding year, and a warm evening. I am stood on Mould Hill in one of my fields, watching a barn owl fly in and out of a pop hole in my neighbour's barn. I can see about 55 red deer hinds in the valley bottom, and my sheep are settling themselves down for the night underneath an old oak tree. The lambs sleep close to the tree trunk, and the ewes round the outside to protect them.

There is so much going on in this valley, it is teaming with life and activity, but I am the only human in the landscape. What an honour it is to be part of this environment, and to work to keep it the way it has been for centuries. I am a small person in a fascinating ecosystem where farmed animals and wildlife co habit and interact, and I feel very privileged to be here, and even more privileged to know that my children will be here when I am gone. Our work is not yet done.

The Day is Done

When my work here is
Handed on,
Because we all know
That work is never done,
Remember to lay me upon
A sheep fleece
As you lower me deep
Into the valley's soil.

Let me clasp a little wool
Between my thumb and finger
Dress me in my working clothes
My old jacket made from
Local tweed,
And woollen socks.
Place my crook upon my coffin
Leave my hat upon its peg.

I will become a part
Of all that I have been
This valley was my world
My heft, my home.
I had no need to wander
Was content within these fells
Now I rest here
Ring fenced, grounded, home.

THE DAY IS DONE

When you pick up stones
To mend the walls
Your hands clasp
Where mine were once.
When you watch the lambs
Running and jumping
In the evening
I built the flock that you tend.

When you lie
On the hay bales
Stacked to the
Roof of the barn,
I shook the seeds that
Renewed that meadow
From hay bales
Many years ago.

I have lived my life as a part
Of this valley
Now I have become
Part of the valley itself.
There is no sorrow in that,
Just renewal, progression
Like the seasons rolling on.
Spring must follow winter.

Glossary

Clipping	shearing
Gan yam	go home
Gimmer	young female sheep
Hogg	lamb of either sex aged between birth and first shearing
In-by land	fields in valley near the farm where sheep can be fed and/or checked daily
Mule	cross bred sheep usually between a fell breed ewe and less hardy breed of tup
Ruddle	red variety of ocher used for marking sheep
Scrow	general mess
Shearling	young sheep that has been sheared once.
Tup	ram or male sheep
Tupping	mating season
Wether	castrated male sheep
Yow	ewe or female sheep

Acknowledgements

This book has a story of its own to tell, thanks to everyone who contributed to its journey towards publication.

Thank you to Dawn Robertson of Hayloft Books for reading my collection of poems, and suggesting that I try to write in prose. Thanks to her for sticking with me throughout the journey of finding my voice as a writer culminating in the publication of this book.

Thank you to Jamie Normington of Cumbria Wildlife Trust for inviting me to speak at a Cumbria Wildlife Trust conference on the theme 'The Lake District is not sheep-wrecked', and to Matthew Kelly, Professor of History at Northumbria University, for suggesting that I rework that lecture into an article for the *Guardian*. Thank you to the *Guardian* for publishing the article, and to my friend Sean Fishpool for reading each chapter as I expanded the article into a book. Thank you to Sean for suggesting that the poems I had written could go between the chapters 'like delicious treats between courses at a restaurant'. Thank you to Eileen Jones for reading the competed book and offering encouragement and help with publicity.

Thank you to my aunt and uncle for the opportunity to visit their farm as a child, and for reading the book and encouraging me. Thanks to my parents, husband and children for their commitment to our farming projects, for sharing my vision and working together. Unfortunately my grandad died before the publication of this book, but thanks must go to him for his inspiring story telling and encouragement. I know he would have approved of this story being told, he loved to read books about local history and farming.

Thank you to Suzanne McNally for the excellent photographs she took of a reluctant subject. I was blessed to find somebody similarly smitten with the parish of Wharton to photograph me there.

Thank you to everybody who rented me land to enable me to keep animals, and thank you to the members of the Rough Fell Sheep Breeders Association who helped us to build up our flock and gave us their time and wisdom, especially to the Capsticks at Birkhaw and to Ben Williams, secretary of the society. Thank you also to my Twitter followers @ruslandvalley who have brightened many dark winter days with their comments, and chivvied me along to publish this book.

Last but not least, thank you to all my neighbours and especially to all the farmers in the Rusland and Crake Valleys who have helped me out over the last seven years. When you are a 'one woman band' sometimes you need to ask for help. When I asked for help it was always forthcoming. It's a wonderful thing to be an independent hill farmer, but it's an even more wonderful thing to be part of a community of such individuals, friends that you can call upon at any time of day or night and know that they will come and help you solve a problem.

I would also like to thank you, the reader, for listening to my story and very much hope you've enjoyed it. The story will continue in the next book about a year in the life of a traditional Lakeland farm.

Read More...

books by Andrea Meanwell

In My Boots, A Year on a Lake District Farm,
978-1-910237-24-3

Lakelanders,
Stories and poems about living in a Lake District valley
978-1-910237-46-5

Four Seasons on a Westmorland Farm
978-1-910237-57-1
(to be published 2019)